# ECHOES OF CHINESE HISTORY

Plate 1. *Chinese golden dragon rising from the mists of antiquity*

# ECHOES of CHINESE HISTORY

Transcribed in the Words and Paintings of
## HOPE WILLIS RATHBUN

CHARLES E. TUTTLE COMPANY: Publishers
Rutland, Vermont & Tokyo, Japan

Representatives
Continental Europe: Boxerbooks, Inc., Zurich
British Isles: Prentice-Hall International, Inc., London
Australasia: Paul Flesch & Co., Pty. Ltd., Melbourne

*Published by the Charles E. Tuttle Company, Inc.*
*of Rutland, Vermont & Tokyo, Japan*
*with editorial offices at*
*Suido 1-chome, 2–6, Bunkyo-ku, Tokyo, Japan*

*Library of Congress Catalog Card No. 66–25437*

PRINTED IN JAPAN

*To the beloved heroes of the San Kuo*
LIU PEI, KUAN YU AND CHANG FEI
*May their spirits someday return*
*To bring back to us*
*All the glories of the Han*

# INTRODUCTION

Mrs. Rathbun was born in Washington, D.C. in 1885 and educated there. She took her A.B. degree at Smith College 1907 with Phi Beta Kappa for her scholarship. In 1907-8, she attended the Sorbonne, Paris and later travelled widely in France for nearly a year studying the architecture and the great galleries.

She comes of a family of world travellers on more than one side. The Grinnells owned whaling ships out of New Bedford and packet boats to England and spoke casually of having lived in Macao. On her father's side, the Willises owned newspapers in Portland, Maine and in Boston during the Revolution, the "Independent Chronicle," considered by the Library of Congress to be one of the best sources of Revolutionary history. Her great grandfather at seventeen was one of the "Indians" in the Boston Tea Party. Her grandfather Nathaniel Parker Willis, was the poet and writer well known in New York in the middle 19th century. He lived in England and France after his graduation from Yale in 1829 and travelled as far as Constantinople where, as he tells the story, he tried to buy a Circassion slave.

Mrs. Rathbun's first memories of art were the iron and gold Japanese sword guards on the parlor mantel. But her lasting interest in the Far East was aroused when she was fourteen and read all of Lafcadio Hearn's books and Fenollosa's *Epochs of Chinese and Japanese Art*.

In 1903-4 her father, the well known geologist Dr. Bailey Willis, was sent to China by the Carnegie Institution of Washington. She was to have gone as his secretary but it was considered too dangerous since it was so soon after the Boxer Rebellion. He went almost to the Tibetan border and came down through Shensi and Szechwan, returning east by the Yangtze.

A few years later, caught up by the fascination of Ancient China, Mrs. Rathbun began intensive study of Chinese culture from many sides, and it became her life interest for fifty years.

She has painted nearly a hundred pictures of Chinese history and lectured on Chinese subjects several times to the American University Women and to a group at the Library of Congress and to the District Association of Phi Beta Kappa. Her writing includes a book of poems *Offerings to Little Gods,* and several articles, one on the background of Chinese ceramics for the Chemistry Magazine of Science Service.

She herself says of *Echoes of Chinese History,* "it is a distillation of fifty years of study with a wish to bring before Americans something of the variety and fascination and scintillating quality of Ancient China."

EDWARD R. PLACE, President
Phi Beta Kappa Association
in the District of Columbia

# CONTENTS

|  |  | *Text* | *Plate* |
|---|---|---|---|
| 1. | Chinese Golden Dragon | 12 | 2 |
| 2. | Shen Nung with his Oxen | 12 | 13 |
| 3. | Cock and Hen on Emperor's Drum | 14 | 15 |
| 4. | Shun's Wives Mourning at River Side | 14 | 17 |
| 5. | Ta Yu at the Yellow River | 16 | 19 |
| 6. | Bronze Worker of the Shang Dynasty | 18 | 21 |
| 7. | Chou Hsin and T'a Chi Beside Pool of Wine | 18 | 23 |
| 8. | Pao Szu, Bewitching Beauty | 22 | 25 |
| 9. | Laotze, a Shadowy, Mystic Figure | 24 | 27 |
| 10. | The Great Sage Confucius | 26 | 29 |
| 11. | Mang Chih Fang's Valiant Retreat | 26 | 31 |
| 12. | Chuang Tzu Chiding Court Official | 28 | 33 |
| 13. | Magic Horse of Shuan-Ti | 30 | 35 |
| 14. | Chang Chien in the Gobi Desert | 32 | 37 |
| 15. | Magic Horses of Ferghana | 32 | 39 |
| 16. | Spirit of the Lady Wang | 34 | 41 |
| 17. | Lady Feng and the Bear | 34 | 43 |
| 18. | Chao Fei Yen, the Flying Swallow | 36 | 45 |
| 19. | Maiden of the Peony Garden | 38 | 47 |
| 20. | Lute Playing in Cold Palace | 40 | 49 |
| 21. | Audience of Chao Chün | 44 | 51 |
| 22. | Chao Chün Among the Hsiung-Nu | 50 | 53 |
| 23. | Chao Chün Hunting with the Khan | 50 | 55 |
| 24. | The Scholarly Lady P'an Chao | 54 | 57 |
| 25. | Liu Pei in the Palace Garden | 58 | 59 |
| 26. | Kuan Yu, the Perfect Warrior | 60 | 61 |
| 27. | Chang Fei, Rough and Ready Warrior | 60 | 63 |

28. Ts'ao Ts'ao, Villian, Scholar, Poet ................... 62    65
29. Liu Pei Leaps the River Tan ........................ 64    67
30. Ssuma-Hui in the Mulberry Tree ..................... 66    69
31. Sun I's Wife Entraps Kwei Lan .................... 68    71
32. The Ladies Chiao Eavesdropping ..................... 70    73
33. Obtaining Weapons by Strategy ..................... 74    75
34. Chuko Liang in Burma ............................ 76    77
35. Menghua's Surrender to Chuko Liang .............. 82    79
36. Azure Banners of Liu Pei ......................... 84    81
37. Mu Lan, Intrepid Fighter ......................... 86    83
38. Chang Seng Yü and the Painted Dragon .............. 88    85
39. Meng Hao Jan in Search of Spring .................. 90    87
40. Yang Ti's Interrupted Game of Chess .............. 92    89
41. Tribute of the Uighurs ......................... 94    91
42. Wen Chen Shocked by Shamanistic Rites ............. 96    93
43. Princess Wen Chen Deified ......................... 96    95
44. Wu Hou, Ruthless, Wise and Just ................... 98    97
45. Yang Kwei Fei on a White Horse .................100    99
46. Yang Kwei Fei Dancing on the Terrace ...............100    101
47. The Tribute Horse ..........................102    103
48. Manjusri's Miraculous Appearance ...............104    105
49. Hui Tsung in the Palace Garden ...............108    107
50. Hui Tsung in Exile ..........................108    109
51. Hsiao Chao Encounters Li Tang ...................110    111
52. Wan Kuei Fei, a Gentle Soul .................114    113
53. Chinese Junk Sailing into Sunrise...................116    115

# ECHOES OF CHINESE HISTORY

ND Chuang-tzu, the Taoist, said to his disciple, "I shall speak to you at random and do you listen to me at random."

It must indeed be so in these tales of ancient time for they are but footnotes to the long years of Chinese history.

There is no beginning and no end. The Chinese dragon rose from the mists of myth so very long ago. Dim figures move in a fog of legend, never wholly seen and with only a few bones or a shard of pottery to keep them company. There is a god who made men, fashioning them from clay, but presently got tired of the effort and dipped bits of hemp in the mud. These were not so successful and made only weaklings and misshapen men. There were kings who lived several hundred years and heroes who shot arrows into the sky against flaming suns.

A people definitely Chinese, and distinguished from the tribes which emerged from the forests of far northeast Siberia, seems to have dwelt south of the Yellow River from time immemorial. If they came from elsewhere, we have no record that can be read.

*Shen Nung with His Oxen*
*(plate 2)*

From them appears about 2600 B.C. the youthful figure of Shen Nung who taught the tribes agriculture and gave them a more abundant harvest than the chance wild grains had offered and led them to form their family clans into larger groups. The earliest poem that in song has come down to us is the proud boast of the husbandman

*Work with the sun*
*Sleep with its setting*
*Dig for my drink*
*Plow for my food.*
*What need I care*
*For the powers above.*

The agriculture was of the most primitive type, the turn of a furrow by a simple wooden hoe. The harvest was left to the chance fortune of sun, and wind, and rains. But still the tribes prospered and Shen Nung was honored and later deified. He is variously pictured, sometimes as an old man in long robe and scholar's cap, his hoe in one hand and a bunch of

Plate 2. *Shen Nung, who taught the Chinese agriculture, 2600* B.C., *with his oxen*

millet in the other. But in the frescoes of northwestern China he is painted as a youth with his two gay oxen drawing a plow. Among the frescoes are interested peacocks, a colorful note.

Shen Nung stands on the threshold of the coming civilization which in the next few hundred years broadens and deepens and affirms its own genius.

There were the years of Yao and Shun, looked back to by the later sages as the golden age to which they longed to return. Yao was a wise and peaceful king, loved and trusted by the people. It is said that an attractive woman could walk across the whole country alone yet unmolested. A bundle, even of value, could be left by the roadside and would be found by its owner, untouched when he sought it a month later. Any citizen, however humble, might petition the Emperor and sound the drum in front of the palace. But so peaceful and contented were the people that the drum was never struck and a cock and a hen roosted there and when the sun rose of a morning, the cock sounded his challenge from it.

*Cock and Hen on Emperor's Drum (plate 3)*

Because his son was a weakling, Yao sought a worthy successor to his rule and found him in a countryman, Shun, making pottery on the banks of the Yellow River. Shun was the filial son of a family who despised and even hated him for his virtues and Yao felt he would make a firm and excellent ruler. He gave him his two daughters in marriage and associated him with himself in the government. There is a most lovely sarcophagus, delicately incised, showing the marriage of Shun to the two girls, a stately scene, the actors in long elaborate robes against the background of the palace. Yao died in old age and Shun became the Emperor. They lived simply in those days and he was father to his people and cared for their welfare, following zealously Yao's precepts. Shun and his two young wives made ready eagerly for a tour of the kingdom to assure themselves of its prosperity. Then by the River Hsiao tragedy struck and Shun was accidentally drowned. The two women wept on the riverbank and stretched imploring arms over its flood. Their tears spotted even the bamboo around them and the leaves changed color at their grief. To this day the variegated bamboo grows indigenously only there on the banks of the Hsiao River where Shun's wives wept for him and then in their desolation, threw themselves into its waters.

*Shun's Wives Mourning at River Side (plate 4)*

Plate 3. *Cock and hen on the emperor's drum*

Ta Yu, in 2205 B.C., became the first Emperor of the Hsia dynasty. He was also the first engineer of China. He had been appointed by the Emperor Shun to undertake the work of draining the land inundated by a flood of the Yellow River. It had caused untold misery, as the periodic inundations have ever since, where the river flowing in a flat plain often changes its course. It was a stupendous task which Ta Yu undertook and was only accomplished in nine years of struggle. He married, but left his wife after four days, not to return till his work on the river was completed. He knew, however, of the birth of his son and twice came near enough to his home to listen to the voices of his wife and tiny son playing in the garden.

For his gift of safety to the people, he was known as the Great Yu and even centuries later the children sang a song in their play: *"But for the great Yu, we should all have been fishes."*

The Hsia dynasty lasted till about 1700 B.C. when the Shangs, a border tribe to the west, came into power.

The Shangs were a brilliant people. The invention of writing in China was theirs. Their government was well organized along feudal lines with the Court and nobles and the mass of the people below them engaged in agriculture. There were also slaves, taken in war with neighboring tribes, sometimes used in menial work. The women if attractive became concubines of their conquerors, but the leading men of the enemy were sacrificed in ancestor worship of the Shangs.

There was a dominating belief in magic and what writing is left chiefly concerns divination in answer to questions by the Emperor. The queries were of many kinds, asking what would be the success of a military expedition, what of the crops for the year, would there be rain or drouth, how many animals would be bagged in the Court's proposed hunt. These questions were incised on bones or the carapaces of tortoises in rather vivid pictographs. Then there were more personal questions, the length of the Emperor's life (surely no magician would dare to predict less than a thousand prosperous years!), the welfare of a favorite wife in childbirth, and would the child be the hoped-for son. The emperor Wu Ti had a toothache and demanded which of his ancestors had wished it on him.

Plate 4. *Shun's wives mourning beside the River Hsiao*

The ancestral spirits could be benevolent or hostile, wherefore the sacrifices to them.

It was a luxurious Court who wore garments of wool and silk with jewelled buttons and fitted to the figure. Their horses and chariots had bronze ornaments and their banners were held at the base of the standards by superb bronze animals. Cowrie shells were used for barter and were treasured. One king gave to each of his daughters two cowrie shell necklaces.

One of the delights of the Court was the hunt. They used bows and arrows and had beaters to bring in the game, and drove to the great hunts in two-horse chariots. There are numerous lists of successful hunts in which hundreds of animals were killed. Some were taken alive and the kings kept private zoos in which the animals were cared for and visited by the king, the noblemen and their ladies.

*Bronze Worker of the*
*Shang Dynasty*
*(plate 6)*

But the great achievement of the Shangs and the one which, owing to its nature, has come down to us intact, was their bronze casting. These splendid vessels were used for ceremonial purposes, for sacrifices to the gods and given as wedding gifts on special occasions to king or nobleman. They are marvellously intricate in ornamentation and superbly wrought with squared edges even in the finest detail. No bronze work has ever surpassed them and we can enjoy their beauty today even as the Shangs did, for there is one great collection and numerous individual pieces in this country. Most charming of all perhaps is a wine vessel, a pensive elephant with a smaller one on his back and his skin in eleborate scrolls.

*Chou Hsin and T'a Chi*
*Beside Pool of Wine*
*(plate 7)*

But the Shangs were not always good neighbors apparently, particularly when their great hunts of several hundred men proved devastating to the holdings of nearby tribes. One of these, the Chiang whose name meant "sheepherder" was excessively irked and joined the Chous for the downfall of the Shang Court. What brought the climax was the wickedness of Chou Hsin, the last Shang Emperor. He seems to have been a complex character who, with some learning and considerable eloquence, used to cover up the extravagance of his conduct as a means of getting his determined way. But his lust, his orgies and his cruelty were too much to be borne. He was abetted or perhaps more truly, led by his infamous concubine

Plate 5. *Ta Yu, China's first engineer, beside the Yellow River which he harnessed*

T'a Chi. She was of the Yusu tribe to the north and he had taken her in a raid. She was of great beauty and charm but almost bestial in spirit. She easily deposed the rightful Queen, and people who opposed her met death in horrible ways, as roasting tied to a copper pillar with fire inside. The orgies she carried on with Chou Hsin and some of the Court were unspeakable and the sober sense of the people was shocked by the pool of wine, really millet beer, in which T'a Chi and Chou Hsin and the strident laughing courtiers bathed naked. Here she stands with Chou Hsin beside the gleaming pool.

The Chous attacked and Chou Hsin perished in the flames of his palace. T'a Chi was taken prisoner by Wu Wang, the leader of the rebels. But her beauty was so fascinating and she held herself so haughtily, no one could be found to strike her down. At length T'ai Kung, the aged councillor of Wu Wang, stepped forward, shuddering, and covering his face with one hand, dealt the fatal blow.

The Chous had been one of the periphery tribes on the kingdom of the Shangs and had less finish, but they soon absorbed much of the Shang culture. They were great organizers and many of the principles of government laid down in those older days became a guiding cord through all of Chinese history until the fall of the Empire and induction of the Republic in 1912.

However, feudalism became their danger. The nobles with their large holdings were strong enough to set themselves up as lesser kings in their own right and clash with the central government to whom they owed feodality. It seems to have been a curious mixture of a high degree of civilization, far beyond the European at that time, with barbarous practices as in the sacrifice of wives and retainers and their attendant animals at the death of a king or an important nobleman. Magic continued to hold them in thrall and perhaps the doom of the Western Chous is the most curious case of it.

Far back in the weakening years of the Hsia dynasty, two spirits of earlier rulers of the state of Pao took on the forms of dragons and entered the palace of the king. In fright, the king and nobles called on the magicians to divine the portent. Should they try to kill the dragons whom

Plate 6. *Bronze worker of the Shang Dynasty*

they recognized as spirits of the older kings or to placate them and if so, how? The answer on the tortoise carapace was "Bid them spit." This was done with due ceremony and the dragons, satisfied departed. But the foam of their mouths was put into an ornamented coffer and carefully kept on the altar of the ancestors and never opened. Through Hsia, Shang, and into the days of Chou, it was inviolate. Then when king Li held the throne, the legend had faded and curiosity got the better of discretion. The spittle flowed from the box into the far confines of the palace and near the entrance of the women's quarters, met a pretty girl of seven and surrounded her, then receded. King Hsuan came to the throne and the child became a woman. Finding herself pregnant for no human reason, the young mother bore the child, a girl beautifully formed, but had it abandoned on the hills.

Now for some time small boys sang at their play songs which were supposed to hold some grain of truth. They sang of an old man and woman who should come through the city carrying a basket for quivers and a bow of mulberry wood and such an event "will be the end of Chou." The seeming prophecy greatly troubled the mind of the king and when an old man and woman appeared in the city selling baskets and bows of the mulberry, they were taken by his orders and imprisoned. The king intended to execute them but they made good their escape and fled from the city. In the lonely hills they heard a baby's wail and came upon the abandoned child wrapped in a silken cover as if precious even though cast out. Taking up the tiny girl, the old man and woman fled further to the state of Pao. Here the baby grew up into a woman of great beauty. The ruler of Pao had seen and bought her, but her exceptional qualities had so impressed him that she was given a training fit for a person of higher position. Later the ruler of Pao fell into some disgrace with king Wu now ruling the Western Chous and as a peace offering sent to him Pao Szu for concubine. Her beauty captivated the king and she became his favorite. When she bore him a son, the child supplanted the heir, son of the rightful Queen, in his father's affections. The true heir was sent to his maternal grandfather, the Marquis of Shen whose fury at the insult smoldered until opportunity should come to take vengeance.

Meanwhile king Wu dallied with the beauty in his palace and neglected

*Pao Szu*
*Bewitching Beauty*
*(plate 8)*

Plate 7. *Chou Hsin, last emperor of the Shang Dynasty, mid 12th century* B.C., *with the wicked T'a Chi, beside the pool of millet "wine" in which they swam*

the kingdom. Only one trait of Pao Szu distressed him. She was of a serious, almost melancholy disposition. She never smiled, much less laughed aloud and her interest in any amusement the Court offered was momentary. The king tried everything, elaborate dances, mountebanks, the Court ceremonials, rich gifts, still she seemed withdrawn into an inner world. Then an idea came to him, fires against the night, the spectacle of watch fires on the mountains to call an alarm to his vassals and troops. It was such a gorgeous sight. So the watch fires were lit and Pao Szu's interest quickened and she laughed aloud delightedly and turned in joyous mood to the king. She was but half human remember and the blood of the dragons stirred in her the desire for vengeance of the ancient kings against the Chous. The troops came in at the summons of the fires but of course there was no enemy for them to meet. But king Wu was overjoyed at the success of his ruse and so repeated it again and again until the troops wearied of the call that came to nothing. So the way was opened for the vengeance of the Marquis of Shen and when the watch fires were lit on the hills with desperate purpose at the attack, no protecting troops appeared. The nobles failed to rally, they had been tricked too many times. King Wu perished in an attempted flight and the eerie laughter of Pao Szu floated over the invaded City of Loyang.

The rightful heir of King Wu came to the Chou throne and there were still the Eastern Chous, but the several hundred years after were marked by a decline in power and turbulence among the smaller kingdoms with less and less subservience to the central government.

It was a period of political disorder and disintegration. Yet it was also the age of the great philosophers and one of the most glorious of Chinese thought.

*Laotze, a Shadowy, Mystic Figure (plate 9)* Laotze, the founder of Taoism, is but a shadowy figure, his doctrines were not written till three hundred years later, yet they have been one of the three great influences in Chinese philosophy. The core of his teaching is mystical and concerns the T'ao which is the divine effluence throughout all things and must be sought by man in his innermost self in passivity and contemplation, precluding activity and organization such as formal government. Above all it expressed unity with Nature. It was hardly a

Plate 8. *Pao Szu, bewitching beauty, thrilled by the watch fires*

doctrine to appeal to any but lonely thinkers, recluses from the world. Yet as time went on Taoism added accretions of a great number of gods, happy ones, and helpful to mankind. The people who would have had no interest in its first esoteric doctrines turned to it and superstitious magic added to its popularity.

The gracious figure of Si Wang Mu entertaining the gods and sages in her fairy palace of the Kuen Lun Mountains, the Eight Immortals, ever on guard for mankind against evil, the kindly god of longevity, Shu Lao sometimes represented by Laotze himself, are all Taoist gods. Yet more than one emperor accidentally committed suicide drinking what proved to be poisonous concoctions in search for the elixir which was to make him immortal.

*The Great Sage Confucius* *(plate 10)*

Of the great sage Confucius, Kung Fu Tzu, how dares a mere story teller speak? He was born in 551 B.C. and in the turbulence of the Warring States, his doctrine that of order and harmony in the conduct of life, the completely upright man, was never found in reality but was the ideal of countless generations after him. It is interesting to note that the Kungs claim descent from the ancient kings of Shang and Confucius, present descendant, was honored in a great celebration a few years ago.

But though a teller of tales may hardly be bold enough to praise the Master, he would venture on one story that adds the charm of humor to his character. Confucius was born in the State of Lu in Shantung and in a few lines of the Analects tells of a young officer of Lu whose name, except for that, would never have been known. In some battle to the north, Mang Chih Fang led a few hundred troops against the enemy and was defeated. Staying in the post of danger at the rear of his small army, he held out alone while his men made their getaway. Praised later for his bravery, he quipped and answered "Oh, it wasn't my doing. My horse was too lazy to run!" As you can see, the frantic horse which he curbs sharply disproves his statement. Confucious praises Mang taking pleasure in his bravery. It is rather amusing that Legge who over two thousand years later made such an excellent translation of the Analects, said in an indignant note "But the man lied. Why did Confucious praise him?" I am afraid Legge was straight-laced!

*Mang Chih Fang's* *Valiant Retreat* *(plate 11)*

Plate 9. *Laotze, a shadowy, mystic figure*

Another great philosopher was the ardent follower of Laotze who set down and amplified his tenets. Chuang Tzu is even more abstruse, one must read him with reason held in reserve but he was a very shrewd old gentleman. He had retired from the world and a Court official who sought

*Chuang Tsu*
*Chiding Court Official*
*(plate 12)*

him out at the Emperor's behest for the ruler wanted him as minister, found him cooling his feet in a mountain brook. Chuang Tzu obdurately refused to come and when the official pressed him, exclaimed impatiently, "Look here, you have a gilded carapace of a tortoise, wrapped in silk and reverently kept in the palace. It is used for divination. But it has been dead for many years. I am sure it would much rather be alive and wagging its tail in the mud like that one near by me, than wrapped in silken wrappings. Begone! I too would rather wag my tail in the mud."

In these difficult times which lasted two hundred and sixty years, small principalities turned into kingdoms warred with each other increasingly and the philosophers theorized and wandered up and down the land trying in their several ways to bring some tranquility but with little effect. There were fifteen or more states struggling to become powerful enough to establish themselves as a supreme central power over their neighbors and the fortunes of war gave first one and then another some ascendancy but never sufficient. It was the state of Ch'in in the west which after successful campaigns against the barbarians, west and south of them, turned covetous eyes on the central Chinese states and in 259 B.C. swept into power.

Shih Huang-ti, the First Emperor as he styled himself, destroyed not only the kingdoms but the last of the ancient feudal system in China. His hope was that with the past destroyed, his own empire would last "ten thousand years" till the end of time. Such was his arrogant determination and he died in 210 B.C. having been for thirty-seven years ruler of Ch'in and eleven of all China's kingdoms. He was not to know that his son would reign but four years before the Ch'in empire would be utterly overthrown and his family exterminated. Shih Huang-ti was a devastating reformer, changing the customs of the people wholesale and wiping out the power of the aristocracy. But he gave order to the writing of Chinese characters and this act became a bond of unity for all China.

Plate 10. *Kung Fu Tzu, known as the great sage Confucius*

The "Great Emperor" was execrated by future generations for his "burning of the books." His aim was to destroy all history before him. Much was lost that would have been of inestimable value to later scholars, but still the destruction has been exaggerated and more was hidden and saved than was acknowledged.

Shih Huang-ti is equally well known and in this case honored for the building of the Great Wall against the outer barbarians who never ceased to be a danger on the northwestern frontier through most of China's history. Parts of the wall had already been built across the passes leading to the Mongolian steppe, but Shih Huang-ti built to the sea and then westward to the border of his own state of Ch'in, the extraordinary distance of 1400 miles. Thousands of men worked endlessly upon it, and many hundreds, perhaps thousands, died in its erection under driving taskmasters.

*Magic Horse of Shuan-Ti (plate 13)*

But a happier story is told as legends grew up around the "First Emperor." It is not surprising that magical aids were attributed to him. He possessed a Magic Horse which helped build the Great Wall leading the men across the mountains and the desert toward the western goal.

But one evening the men lingered over their meal talking of their distant homes and the difficulties of labor in the desert mountains. Unnoticed the Magic Horse veered off and was lost to sight among the hills. Next morning they took the direction they supposed it had followed and labored at their task of building. But no horse appeared and they were forced to turn and search. When they found him far away, munching the scarce grass of the steppes, it was in an entirely different direction and the Magic Horse eyed them almost malevolently. So the men built the wall along the direction of the Horse's course and most of it stands today. But still stands also forty miles of Great Wall leading out into the desert where only a few birds fly. It has no purpose. It is but a monument to an error and an hour's gossip of two thousand years ago.

When the weakling son of Shih Huang-ti lost the Empire which was to last ten thousand ages, it was Liu Pang, a former peasant, who came into power as the Emperor Kao Tsu. He had been an adventurer and answered someone who reproached him for his hostility toward the schol-

Plate 11. *Mang Chih Fang, 500 B.C., officer of Lu, whom Confucius praised for protecting his troops after defeat. Mang laughingly replied, "Oh it wasn't I, my horse was too lazy to run!"*

ars, "What have I to do with them? I won my Empire on horseback and so I will keep it." He was forced to reward his adherents and so partially restored feudalism and it was not until 127 B.C. that he could take absolute control of the country. There is a superb picture in the Boston Museum of Fine Arts of Liu Pang entering his capital city of Chang-an in Wei with banners flying and fair ladies at the palace grouped to greet him.

*Chang Chien in the Gobi Desert (plate 14)*

The greatest monarch of the Han was the Emperor Wu Ti 140 B.C. He extended the borders of the Empire, even conquering Szechwan and wild Yunnan to the southwest and far beyond the Great Wall brought the northern part of the Korean peninsula under his sway. One of his generals, Chang Chien, was sent west to persuade certain tribes to aid the Emperor in subduing the Hsiung-Nu, later called the Huns, who for centuries harassed China's northern borders. Twice he fell captive to the Hsiung-Nu but escaped and going ever westward reached the Oxus river. Long later he returned with only one of the followers who had set out with him, and a Tartar wife. Thus Chang Chien brought back immense new knowledge of Central Asia and embassies were sent to a number of the tribes and the influence of China was felt as far as Bactria.

*Magic Horses of Ferghana (plate 15)*

So it was at this time that the Magic Horses of Ferghana in Turkestan were imported for the Emperor Wu Ti. They were thirty superb stallions and legend had it that they were not born, but rose from a lake in central Turkestan. They were magic indeed, swift as the wind and with splendid manes and tails, and held their heads high in pride of their breed. The Emperor who loved beauty and appreciated their finer points, rejoiced greatly in their possession. One magic trait they had which struck awe into the Chinese. When the horses were galloped or in a sweat, they returned with drops of blood on their necks. They did not seem to be harmed but strange magic must be behind it. Modern science has unearthed the mystery. In Ferghana there is a tiny parasite which burrows under the skin and when the animal is heated, causes minute blood vessels to burst. Perhaps the real magic lay in the fact that the horses did not suffer.

Wu Ti surrounded himself with beauty and splendour. His palaces

Plate 12. *Chuang Tzu chiding the court official*

stretched for over a mile lifting their curved roofs over carved eaves, red and gold in the morning light. His parks filled with rare trees and shrubs extended far and wide on all sides and there the courtiers hunted deer and even sometimes braved the tiger.

But there were other sides to life even at the luxurious court. Wu Ti was an ardent Taoist and sought the elixir of immortality and his magicians were versed in magic practices. But magic could not hold death from those the Emperor loved. The exquisite Lady Wang was dead and the Emperor mourned for her and would not be consoled. She had gladdened so many hours. In vain he importuned powerful magicians. Then at last a younger magician begged him to enter a shrouded alcove. The gold embroidered curtains with their leaping dragons were drawn back and

*Spirit of the Lady Wang*
*(plate 16)*

above an adorned altar rose a mist of incense. Dimly blue it rose in the low lights spiraling toward the gilt rafters. Slowly there emerged an indistinct form, then deepened. Richly colored robes fell in graceful folds around a slight figure and, as the Emperor held his breath a wistful face appeared above them and before him floated the spirit of the Lady Wang. Her dark eyes sought his and a slight smile wavered on her lips. The Emperor started forward, but slowly the image faded. All in a moment the incense sank and only the flickering lights remained moving against the darkness behind them. The Emperor sighed, his heart torn by that one brief glimpse. At least she had smiled. He would have that memory.

It was when the Emperor Yuan Ti was on the throne 48–33 B.C. that they tell the story of Lady Feng and the bear. Yuan Ti who was fond of animals, had a number in cages along the bank of a stream which flowed through the palace park. For amusement one afternoon he and the Court went out to see them. The Emperor viewed with interest some new arrivals, small chattering monkeys from far to the south, and the court ladies giggled and twittered at their grimaces and quaint posturings. So intent were they that no one noticed a low growl nearby. But suddenly little Lady

*Lady Feng and the Bear*
*(plate 17)*

Feng sprang forward in front of the Emperor. Her arms outstretched, she faced a half grown bear which had broken its cage and leapt down before them. She stood a full minute in front of him, shaking her head at him, the flowered pins of her headdress quivering, while the Emperor, the court

Plate 13. *The magic horse of the Ch'in Emperor Shuan-ti which helped build the Great Wall of China*

ladies and a gouty minister drew back in alarm. The bear gave a rumbling growl but hesitated and in that moment the guards rushed in and prodded him back into his cage. The Emperor, recovering his poise, gave angry orders and then turned to Lady Feng and exclaimed "Why did you do it?" "I thought, Sire, your Majesty was in danger" she answered simply.

*Chao Fei Yen,*
*the Flying Swallow*
*(plate 18)*

A charming figure in the records of the Han is Chao Fei Yen, the dancer. Music and dancing were among the most loved entertainments at the Court and there are many pictures of gayly dressed orchestras playing for the Emperor and the court ladies dancing. Chao Fei Yen was the daughter of a musician and was from a child trained in all the art of dancing. So dainty was she, that as she danced and her scarves floated round her in swift motion and her sleeves far longer than her finger tips circled now her head, now dropped downward almost to her tiny feet, she seemed rather a flying bird with outstretched wings than a woman. So they called her the Flying Swallow and even in Chang-an, used to beauty in diverse forms, people gazed upon her with delight. The Emperor, Cheng Ti, held to the precepts of the golden age and felt as father to his people, sometimes with only a few followers even roaming the capital in disguise. On one such royal jaunt, he came upon the Swallow dancing before a small group of country folk who gaped in wonder at such skill and grace as they had never seen before. The Emperor of course had seen many dancers but none os such exquisite perfection. He lingered long watching her and the end could be foreseen without the telling. Chao Fei Yen left her humble quarters in a side street to become an Emperor's favorite in the palace, even to receive the title of Empress Consort. But the world turned dark when Cheng Ti died a few years later. There were those who bitterly envied the dancer the grace and charm they did not have and it was in 6 B.C. that, beset by court intrigue she could not face, she committed suicide. And there were those too who mourned her for she had become a legend of a flying bird.

North of the Great Wall near the village of Suiyuan, the desert loess flies in dust clouds and the roads are rutted far below the level of the countryside worn by the broad wheeled carts. The land is sear and brown ex-

Plate 14. *Chang Chien in the Gobi Desert*

cept in the brief spring. In its midst a tumulus rises and around it four marble stelae. The mound stays always green above the arid countryround, a memory to a legend two thousand years old. It is the grave of Wang Chao Chün, one of the most loved heroines of China.

When Yuan Ti became Emperor in 48 B.C., the country was peaceful and prosperous under its last wise rulers. Yuan Ti himself was a kindly man devoted to art and music and something of a scholar. On coming to the throne, it was of the country he thought and paid little due to personal pleasures. Then as was natural enough, his mind turned to fair women.

*Maiden of the Peony Garden (plate 19)* On a spring night he dreamt of wandering in a garden under ancient pines and by small rippling cascades. There a sheltered walk was bordered with flowering peonies and coming toward him at a little distance he saw a slight figure in pale rose, her high headdress caught up with butterfly hairpins and her delicate face lit by a smile. The enchantment of her beauty made him catch his breath, but as he started toward her, the vision faded and he was left alone gazing into space. But his waking in the daylight had not effaced the image, the dream still held his longing. If there were not somewhere a reality behind it, why had its seeming presence been vouchsafed him. His ideal had appeared before him, the actuality of the vision must be found, wide search should be made for her. So Yuan Ti called together the more intimate of his courtiers. Among them was the minister, Mao-Yen-Shou, respected and also feared for his clever suavity that hid a deep cunning. He was also the court painter in which he showed rare skill and had won the Emperor's admiration. It was he who offered to search for the maiden of the Emperor's dream, an offer Yuan Ti gladly accepted. But Mao had but one intent in the matter, to add greatly to his own wealth and prestige by the venture. He would find for the Emperor a large number of fair women and the most beautiful would be brought to Yuan Ti's attention as his dream maiden, whether or not she resembled the lady of the vision. If she were sufficiently attractive, she could probably overcome the claims of her dream rival.

It was not difficult to find families and their daughters dazzled by the prospect of court life. Only in one instance was the family reluctant. This was in the household of a scholar prefect named Wang Jang who lived at Ch'i Chow in the province of Hupeh. He and his beloved wife were great-

Plate 15. *The magic horses of Ferhana, imported by the Emperor Wu Ti about 140* B.C.

ly admired and respected and lived quietly with a lovely daughter, Chiang, born in their older age. She was as beautiful as the perfection of white jade and her character matched her beauty. She had been trained in the principles of Confucius and the arts proper to a maiden, particularly in music. With the lute she was most skilful and often accompanied herself in song. Though seventeen she was not married for her parents loved her deeply and she had been unwilling to give up the happy life with them. So it was rather with fear than enthusiasm that they learned of Mao's search and that he had heard of her beauty.

Mao had learned too much and sought them out. His demand was peremptory and backed by the exalted figure of the Emperor. Wang Jang's wife feared court intrigue even more than Wang Jang himself. Mao had not inspired them with confidence, his manner had been crude and bullying. But there was no help for it and they must yield with fearful hearts.

Chiang herself, though trembling and unhappy, did her best to console them and tried to set forth smiling. Mao had already gained a fortune from complacent families and Wang Jang had added a large sum, not in ambition but rather in the hope of his daughter's being given at least kindly consideration. He felt there would be no question of the Emperor's interest if he once saw her.

At Chang-an, Mao presented himself to the Emperor and proclaimed he felt that he had been successful in finding the fairest women in the kingdom and that the lady of the garden would be among them. He was bidden to paint a portrait of each of the many women.

Craftily Mao set about his task and garnered an additional fortune from the bribes which were given him to paint portraits that would enhance their beauty. But the lovely Chiang seemed impervious to hints. She knew her father had given Mao gold and her upright spirit could not conceive the malevolence of the Minister at being balked of added gain. So at first she did not know that he had given her portrait a twist which ruined her charm.

*Lute Playing in the Cold Palace (plate 20)*

The Emperor, therefore, failed to find his vision of the peony garden but chose other women and many for his pleasure. So for three years Chiang spent the long hours of loneliness and lost hopes in the Cold

Plate 16. *Spirit of the Lady Wang*

Palace. There dwelt court ladies whom the Emperor ignored and their life was a dreary one. Luxuriously cared for, up to a point, there seemed no purpose in their existence. Chiang sang and played her lute and lingered often in the inner gardens. One close and happy friend she made, the cheerful Wan Hua, full of common sense and zest for life and not too troubled knowing that her squat figure and face like a full moon could never receive the Emperor's glance. She was however not unaccomplished on the lute, and often the two girls played together or solaced their solitude with song. Wan Hua's devotion and cheerful spirit served somewhat to ease her beloved friend's unhappiness and frustration.

Then events along China's northern border brought together the tangled threads of several lives. For many years, even from middle Chou times, the Hsiung-nu had been a danger to the north. They were a nomad and barbaric tribe living in yurts and moving with their flocks and herds in search of pasture. In peace they hunted and were fine archers but their true profession was war and they were but too adept at it. China felt very constantly the impact of their forays. A quarrel between two brothers of the Hsiung-nu resulted in the death of the elder at Chinese hands and a treaty made with Hu Hanshieh, the younger brother. This was faithfully kept and the border tranquil. The Khan even visited the Han Court and was entranced with its luxury and the suavity of its manners in such contrast to the rough and simple life beyond the Great Wall. So his demand to seal the alliance by being given a Chinese princess as wife did not come as too great a surprise. Though unwelcome, it was not unprecedented, other chiefs had received as brides court ladies of high rank as assurances of peace along the frontier.

So it came about in this instance and Yuan Ti, pondering the matter, determined on Chiang whom he had never seen, but whose portrait he had disdained. It was commanded that her rank be raised to princess, Lady Chao Chün, the Brilliant One, and she would be the bride of the Khan Hu Hanshieh. Yet a too reluctant bride would be a poor envoy as far as China was concerned and in mercy, yet in calculated prudence, word was sent requesting her consent. At first Chao Chün was overwhelmed and despair claimed her. For so long her thought had turned toward the Emperor and a small hope of his sometime favor had lingered. Now she was

Plate 17. *Lady Feng and the bear*

face to face with stark fact. She was not entirely ignorant of what life among the Tartars would be and shuddered at her racing thoughts while the faithful Wan Hua tried to comfort her. But she knew too well what the harassments of the Hsiung-nu had meant and other thoughts succeeded her first shrinking. She was the victim but she was also the chosen one. A brilliant life at court would not be hers, yet to her country and her people she could be useful. So her response though given in a broken voice, was acceptance of a future with the nomads. Gratified at least by her obedience, the Emperor ordered a ceremonial audience to present her to the assembled Court and the Tartar envoys.

Splendid preparations were made. Rare treasures decorated the palace courts and halls. Bronze vessels held flowering plants and bright banners were displayed in profusion, while all the Court was in gayest costume, a contrast to the furs and heavy wools of the bearded envoys of the Hsiung-nu, some of whom peered and squinted at the splendour before them.

There was a hush as Yuan Ti took his seat on the dragon carved throne and gazed with half irritated attention down the hall. It was hard to hand over even an ugly Chinese princess to these rough barbarians. Still he had been mollified by the almost humble memorial to the throne from the Tartar Khan and had answered it in dignified and suitably royal manner with his promise to bestow a princess on the Khan.

*Audience of Chao Chün*
*(plate 21)*

The audience would have grown restless with expectation but they had not long to wait. There was a tinkle of girdle ornaments as the doors opened and a delicate perfume from silk robes spread through the audience hall. A group of young girls surrounded Chao Chün. They carried small lanterns which lit the exquisite beauty and perfection of her features. Her kingfisher headdress glowed above pearl fringed ornaments and her robe was rose crimson lavishly embroidered with phoenixes and rosy clouds. But it was her face which held all eyes. The Tartar envoys stared with open mouths. Surely the Emperor feared their ruler's power if he was willing to bestow such beauty upon him. But the courtiers looked in amazement and dismay, why was the Emperor sending this jewel into the northern wastes?

Chao Chün advanced with quiet step and sank to her knees before Yuan Ti. As he bent forward to raise her, their eyes met and it was a long mo-

Plate 18. *Chao Fei Yen, the Flying Swallow, an exquisite dancer and court favorite*

ment that they gazed. For that short space there might have been no one else in the great hall.

Then the spell broke and Chao Chün turned to face the crowded Court. All gazed as did the Emperor at the lovely girl standing quietly before them. The Hsiung-nu grinned uncouthly in their satisfaction. The Emperor spoke a few words but his voice was strained. When only a few of the courtiers had come forward to bow before the Princess, Yuan Ti's command rang across the audience. In unseemly haste, he dismissed them and giving a curt order to the nearest minister, left the hall. Chao Chün was brought to him in an inner room where he often sat among his beloved books of ancient wisdom. The girl's beauty seemed to glow in even greater perfection against the dark walls as she looked at him with wide eyes. Here was his maiden of the peony garden, only not a dim figure now but a living breathing woman before him. He gazed long at her, then his demands burst forth. What did it mean? Why had he never known of her presence? By whose evil intrigue had she been hidden?

In words that trembled on her lips but grew firmer, she told him of Mao's treachery which drove him to a furious anger rigidly controlled lest she suffer further. Then though the details of Mao's punishment seethed in the back of his mind, he began making plans for her rescue from the fate into which he had thrust her.

Kneeling she listened but shook her head. "Sire, it cannot be. Your royal word is sacred—you have given it. Even the Huns hold honor in esteem. You have made great show and the envoys have seen me. Could someone else pretend to be the offered bride? War would be the answer and they have power to make our people suffer." A shudder overcame her but she went on firmly. "No, fate has decreed for me. At least I can take my part."

She made no further protestation but he saw resolve in her eyes. What did that matter? One fair enough could be found, the envoys could return loaded with treasure, uncouth, their heavy senses could be befuddled. Still she shook her head, as she gazed at him, though her nails, hidden in her long sleeves, bit into her palms.

It was even as she had foretold. The Emperor had not gaged the Huns whom no offer could turn from their pride in being able to bring such a

Plate 19. *Maiden of the Peony Garden*

prize to their Khan. Their exultation over what they thought the weakness of the Emperor in offering them such a jewel, had equalled their amazement and they were like a stone wall. No lure could lead them from their determination.

Unrestful, the Court set about preparations for her going. They lasted a full month and were magnificent—she must have all things that became a Chinese princess.

Wang Chao Chün herself went as if in a trance, obedient to other's plans, her only request that Wan Hua accompany her into the grim northern land. It is said that in those few weeks the shy Empress became fond of her and would have kept her if she could, which speaks for the gentleness of the two women. Wan Hua whose cheerful spirit took the world as it came, looked almost eagerly to exile since she would share it with her beloved friend.

The hours passed but too quickly and the day of departure came. Chao Chün ascended one of the high towers adjoining the palace and overlooking the imperial city and bade it farewell. Then turning toward the home of her girlhood, whispered a message to her unknowing parents. They would but too soon know what had befallen her. Weeping she descended to the royal cart awaiting her, but braced herself for the parting with the Emperor and Empress who blessed her with faltering phrases for her happiness. The Emperor turned away in bitter grief.

Then followed three weary months of travel through the Jade Pass and by the shrine where travellers left offerings for their safe return, which could not be the lot of Chao Chün. Then across forbidding wastes of the Gobi Desert and into the mountains beyond where spring began, brooks flowed in small cataracts and birds sang in fragrant bushes beside the trail. Wan Hua responded with a lift of heart, but Chao Chün found it hard to rise above the sense that each li meant added distance from all she felt dear.

At last the Tartar camp, spread out in a sloping valley, came into view. Her escort led the cavalcade to a huge yurt near a group of lofty spruces, where court ladies of the Khan were waiting to receive her. Chao Chün and Wan Hua fought back their weariness to greet the older women. The black yurt was filled with every luxury the tribe afforded, white felt upon the floor and rugs and wolf skins in profusion, while the walls were bor-

Plate 20. *Wang Chao Chün and her friend Wan-Hua playing their lutes in the cold palace (from an embroidery)*

dered with red lacquered chests. A boiling kettle hung above the dung fire in preparation of the evening meal and two hunting dogs rose from beside it. The girls shrank back and attendants would have cuffed the dogs down, but to the Mongols amazement, the beasts came forward with wagging tails and as Chao Chün sank down upon the cushioned divan, lay down at her feet and licked her hands.

Days of rest and eager hospitality, but oh, how different from the distant courts of Chang-an. The inquisitiveness of even the older women, the whining music of shrill instruments, the constant noises of the busy camp, the whirling smoke above the smoldering fire, all grated upon nerves already frayed. Yet she must brace herself and meet the wedding day with composure. Until the day itself, the Khan had only seen Chao Chün from a distance as custom demanded, but even a glimpse was enough for his elation and also wonder that Yuan Ti had foregone such beauty.

The wedding itself was conducted with propriety and even pomp though hardly with Chinese etiquette. The Khan's excitement grew and would have oppressed Chao Chün beyond bearing, had she not recognized, behind the rugged face and shaggy beard, a certain kindliness and a real effort to smooth her path in strange, even intimidating surroundings. It made her task easier for she was determined to gain from him under oath the firm promise of peace with China and with Yuan Ti. That was accomplished, for the Khan had been sincere and in any case was of no mind to refuse her anything; she could with ease set herself to learn the new ways of life in the high hills.

*Chao Chün Among the Hsiung-Nu (plate 22)*

A certain freedom and directness of approach among the Mongols appealed to her frank nature, but it was long before she could reconcile herself to uncouth manners and the lack of all the small amenities of life in Changan. She and Wan Hua solaced themselves with song and lute which brought sometimes too poignant memories of their lost homeland, but entranced the Khan and his people. Chao Chün was very interested in the women and children and remembering her own gentle upbringing, gave them new ideas and suggested different ways which smoothed their paths.

*Chao Chün Hunting with the Khan (plate 23)*

She bore a son to the aged Khan. Early he showed great promise. He was brought up in a mingling of the two civilizations and while he was

Plate 21. *The audience of Chao Chün*

trained by his father in the free outdoor life of the Hsiung-nu, archery and the use of weapons, the centaur-like riding of superb stallions and the care of herds, he learned something of the great Court of Chang-an which he might hope to see some day and a gentler life than the Mongols could envision. Chao Chün found perhaps a balm for her never forgotten longing to return, in teaching him.

Then the Khan died. She mourned him sincerely for he had been kind. But to learn that by Mongol custom she must marry the next Khan, his handsome and more boisterous son, was a shock she could ill sustain. It was appalling to one brought up in the doctrines of Confucius. She pleaded the period of mourning and sent questioning and longing letters to the Chinese Court. But Yuan Ti had died and an indifferent Emperor answered her plea, brutally bidding her accept the fate she had chosen. It did not prove quite the ordeal she had dreaded. The young Khan had a charm and a certain refinement which his father had lacked and the nearness of their ages made for closer understanding. Two daughters were born to them and Chao Chün delighted in their eager prattle, while the whole court came to love them.

But the years passed too swiftly and her son was still a boy when the second Khan was killed in a hunting accident and another uncle became the ruling Khan.

The grieving Chao Chün still kept her honored place and could make her power felt binding the new Khan to peace with China. It was the goal of her sacrifice long ago and of her whole life. But lives were not long or seldom so among the Hsiung-nu and three Khans came to power and died by the time I-Tu-Chih, her son, was twenty. The peace with China held and Chao Chün lived quietly in retirement. Hardly middle aged, she was still the beauty of the Peony Garden but with a deeper light in her eyes and a kindliness toward her adopted people that made her loved by all and her welfare guarded as an almost sacred thing. Her joy was in her children. It was hard to let her elder daughter go as lady-in-waiting to the Empress Dowager at the Chinese Court but it was a link with the old life and the charming girl would be happier there. Her younger daughter was early married to a minister at the Tartar Court.

So through the reigns of five Khans, Chao Chün had kept by her in-

Plate 22. *Chao Chün among the Hsiung-nu*

fluence the northern borders of China unmolested with a firm peace between the two countries.

But the sixth Khan was of another calibre. Ambition rode him and he wished only to insure the succession to his own son. I-Tu-Chih was next in line and he took early opportunity to have him assassinated.

Dusk was falling across the mountain slopes, the long shadows lit here and there by the dim lights in the yurts, the herds had been brought in and were being milked and the riding stallions champing over their evening meal. Chao Chün, who had been indisposed for a day or two, leant against her cushions listening for the quick step of I-Tu-Chih while the affectionate Wan Hua played softly on a jewelled lute. But the quick step did not come. Instead it was the urgent yet faltering one of an old servant who threw himself sobbing at their feet. Hardly articulate, he told his tale of the murder. A cry burst from Chao Chün and she sank down fainting. The blow had struck too deeply and never fully regaining consciousness she died before the morning.

Her memory, one of the most fragrant in all Chinese history, still lives in the high mountain passes beyond the Gobi and nearer at hand by the Great Wall, the tumulus of her grave stays green even in winter surrounded by the brown reaches of the desert loess.

During the peaceful years of the middle Han, literature, poetry and history flourished and about A.D. 90 Szu-ma Chien wrote his remarkable *Historical Records*. No account of Chinese history is complete without reference to them. The first dictionary was also written at this time. Can one imagine a British chieftain sitting down just after the Roman conquest to indite a dictionary which would be of use a thousand years later?

*Scholarly Lady P'an Chao*
*(plate 24)*

But not only men were proficient in learning. There is the interesting figure of the Lady P'an Chao, noted as the greatest of scholars among the Chinese women. She was a lady-in-waiting of the Empress, and given the title of "Mistress of Poetry, Eloquence and History." Married at fourteen, she was early left a widow and devoted herself to historical studies. The family was a brilliant one and her brother P'an Ku was court historiographer. Sadly enough he fell into disgrace at court and died soon after in prison. It was P'an Chao who completed *The Book of Han* after his death.

Plate 23. *Chao Chün hunting with her husband,
the Khan of the Hsiung-nu, and his son*

And it was also she who wrote the admirable *Admonitions of a Perceptress,* as a guide to the behavior of court ladies. Some of the admonitions seem to us restrictive, but it is interesting to note that she advocated the education of women. Of course she herself was a shining example of it. There is a very beautiful scroll in the British Museum giving phases of the Admonitions. If not by the great painter Ku Kai Chih, it is an early and excellent copy of his work. With practically no backgrounds, the graceful figures flow into one another in the scroll, a vivid and charming picture of court life under the Han. We moderns are sometimes critical over the assiduity of the Chinese in copying the ancient masterpieces, but the actual paintings were fragile, it is amazing that any have survived, and we should be grateful for the excellent early copies.

"Empires wax and wain; states cleave asunder and coalesce," so begins the great novel of the Three Kingdoms written more than a thousand years after the events it portrays.

At the end of the 2nd century A.D., the power of the Han was faltering, its downfall brought about by weak-willed emperors whose court yielded to the power of palace eunuchs, until in turn self-seeking ministers put them down and took control, the emperors mere puppets in their hands. It was a time of disunion and turbulence when nearly every man's hand was against his neighbor. For a century thereafter, three kingdoms fought for supremacy in constant battle. These were Wei which held the remnants of the Han Court and the emperors in pawn under the powerful minister Ts'ao Ts'ao, Shu in the west where Liu Pei a scion of the reigning house struggled to restore the Han power, and Wu in the south which played fast and loose with first one and then another of the other two. The fighting was hard headed enough and guile, deceit and treachery took their part in the hundred years between 168–265 A.D. Yet this time, with its intense struggle for power, its many instances of daring and bold venture and its mighty heroes, became the great period of romance to generations of later Chinese. Fabulous stories grew up around its history and were told by story tellers under the village trees far and wide.

Plate 24. *The Lady P'an Chao, mistress of poetry, eloquence, and history*

It remained for a scholar Lo Kuan Chung to bring these tales together into the *San Kuo Chi Yen I,* the Romance of the Three Kingdoms, one of the great novels of the world. This was in the 14th century and because the novel form was at that time despised by the literati as beneath their notice, it is not even certain that Lo Kuan Chung wrote it. Little is known of him but his name still serves. Certainly none but a scholar could have written its one hundred and twenty chapters. It has been read with joy ever since by scholars who would not have discussed it with their equals, by school boys and indeed by all the Chinese world.

The story opens with a reference to the waning power of the Han and to portents of evil which drove the neurotic Emperor Hsien to seek remedies from his magicians. Unrest throughout the country led to the rise of the Yellow Turbans, a rather blind rebellion which was however widespread and demanded a firm military hand. Notices were posted calling for volunteers and in the district of Cho, one who read them sighed over his individual powerlessness. A distant scion of the royal house, his family had at one time been prominent in the district, but lost its rank and had become poverty stricken. His father Li Hung had been a scholar and a minor official, but had died young, leaving his widow to bring up the ambitious boy. An uncle had aided them, but Liu Pei although well educated had at this time found no outlet for his skills and was making his living as a seller of straw sandals and the weaving of grass mats. A very different person watched him as he read the notice, Chang Fei, a man of substance, wine seller and owner of a farm nearby.

"If you are not willing to help your country, why do you stand sighing?" he asked. His suggestion that they consult on the matter led to their retiring to the village inn, where even as they sat down, a huge fellow entered calling for wine in haste since he was hurrying to join the army. His whole appearance was dignified and impressive, his huge stature and long beard, his keen and flashing eye singled him out as a man of parts. Liu Pei watched him, then courteously crossed over and asked his name.

"I am Kuan Yu, a native from over the river but for some time a fugitive from justice for having killed a brute and a bully who was molesting a young girl. Now I seek to join the army and be of service to my country."

Plate 25. *Liu Pei at sunrise in the palace garden*

Finding themselves of one mind, they were inspired to join hands in their effort to aid the reigning house of Han. This resulted the next morning in the famous Oath of the Peach Garden in which, after proper sacrifice, they took blood oath to be faithful to each other to the death and to perform the possible or impossible to restore the house of Han to its former glories.

Thus are introduced the three heroes of the San Kuo who soon drew to themselves a body of strong men and in the first encounter with the rebels, Liu Pei slew the leader and dispersed the enemy. They were none of them creations of fiction. Indeed the majority of the hundreds of characters in the San Kuo are historical and played their part in the war-like years that followed.

Victory came most often to the sworn brothers but never quite enough, always another city to be stormed or besieged, an ambush to be avoided, an intrigue to be calculated against treacherous wiles, another battle fought.

Liu Pei gained the adherence of Shu and became by title Emperor of Minor Han but he was never really more than king. Here he stands at sunrise in the palace gardens of Szechuan gazing toward Wei where his enemies balked his hopes. He died at sixty-three, broken-hearted at failure to restore the Han, but he has been one of the most loved characters of Chinese history ever since.

*Kuan Yu*
*the Perfect Warrior*
*(plate 26)*

Kuan Yu, the perfect warrior, "terrible in war, in peace the soul of chivalry," is the even more striking figure. His exploits ring with a clarion note through the San Kuo, brilliant strategist, devisor of victories and selfless follower of his sworn brother and lord, he is one whose fascination has seldom been surpassed in history. He has won the admiration of millions down the years and in 1594 was first honored as a god Kuan Ti, a god of war but one who prevents war, not forges it and succors those oppressed, so he is prayed to by the people, a potent force in China even today.

*Chang Fei*
*Rough and Ready Warrior*
*(plate 27)*

The character of Chang Fei is very different and shows how the novel was formed from many differing strands. At the opening of the tale, it is he who brings the three heroes together and is really responsible for the

Plate 26. *Kuan Yu, the perfect warrior*

Oath of the Peach Garden. But as the story continues, he is revealed as the truculent one who must be curbed and without the keeness of the other two. He is the rough and ready warrior, always eager for the fray, probably rather true to the type of the period. In his cups he was at times brutal and his death came about by assassination from one of his own men. But he is very human and absolutely faithful in his devotion to Liu Pei and Kuan Yu.

*Ts'ao Ts'ao,*
*Villain, Scholar, Poet*
*(plate 28)*

The early ally and then arch enemy of the sworn brothers is Ts'ao Ts'ao, the powerful minister of Wei who controls the Court and manipulates the weak emperors for his purposes. He is the villain of the piece, more so perhaps than in actual history, and his success in making himself all powerful, and finally in putting his son on the throne is the tragedy of the novel. He seems to have been something of a scholar and also a poet.

So many are the characters vividly portrayed that even a few lines on each would compass a long book, but after the three brothers, Chuko Liang, the great general and wily minister of Liu Pei stands out as the most interesting figure of the period.

He first comes into the tale as a recluse whom Liu Pei seeks, having heard of his wisdom and acuteness. He proves hard to reach and difficult to persuade but presently throws himself wholeheartedly into the cause of the sworn brothers and after their deaths, into the protection of Liu Pei's son until his own death. He even has himself perpetuated as a statue to strike awe into the enemy for a little time.

Such incidents as we may glean are but drops in the ocean compared with the splendid sweep and surge of the novel itself, but they must serve as they may.

Surely we must begin with a feat of Liu Pei. At one time he was defeated in battle with Ts'ao Ts'ao's forces and forced to take refuge in Ching-chou, a city held by a distant cousin Liu Piao, who received him very kindly. They discussed the possibility of entering the capital while Ts'ao Ts'ao was in the north on an expedition, but Liu Piao feared the attempt. He seemed to be secretly depressed and Liu Pei questioning him, found him troubled about his two sons. The elder who would naturally

Plate 27. *Chang Fei, rough and ready warrior, one of the three heroes of the* Tales of the Three Kingdoms

succeed him was physically a weakling and the younger by his second wife more fitted to be prefect. However the law of primogeniture should hold and in that case Liu Piao feared the intrigues of the Lady Tsai and her family who had power with the army of Ching-chou. Liu Pei strongly advised him not to set aside his first born son. The Lady Tsai was listening behind the curtains and naturally conceived an intense resentment for Liu Pei since his advice ran so fiercely counter to her ambitions for her own son. She plotted with her brother Tsai Mao who controlled the army. A harvest festival at Hsiang Yang nearby gave them their opportunity since Liu Piao who was not well had asked Liu Pei to preside.

Liu Pei had ridden in with an escort of three hundred men and his general Chao Yün, but these had been lured away to a feast in another part of the city and only a faithful follower I Chi remained with him at the banquet. However I Chi had been on the alert and overheard the plotters so that he had Liu Pei's superb horse Tilu, which had been captured in battle, tethered near at hand. Entering the banquet hall where Liu Pei was playing the host with dignity and charm, I Chi approached him with a wine cup and, giving him a warning look, whispered "Make an excuse to get away!" Liu Pei who had not been entirely deceived by the over-insistent courtesy of Lady Tsai's brother, rose as if stiff with sitting too long and went outside where he found I Chi waiting with Tilu. He was startled, however, as I Chi told him of the plot and that all gates were guarded except the western one which led only to the river Tan whose swift current was impassable. Grabbing Tilu's bridle, he made a leap into the saddle and galloped off. Reaching the west gate the few guards there would have stopped him but he rode through them at a furious pace. Uncertain what to do they retired into the city for orders and Liu Pei reached the bank of the Tan. It looked hopeless, its current swift and turbulent and Liu Pei turned back. But prusuit was in sight in a cloud of dust and he turned again toward the dangerous river and plunged in. Tilu struggled a few paces but seemed floundering and his rider exclaimed desperately "Tilu, Tilu, I trust to you." Suddenly Tilu reared and with one tremendous leap made the western bank. It was as if they had reached up into the clouds and come down again.

Looking back, Liu Pei saw his pursuers gathered on the other side of

Plate 28. *Ts'ao Ts'ao, villain, scholar, poet*

the river. They called demanding to know why he had left the feast.

"Why did you wish me injury?" answered Liu Pei.

"We wished you none," but at the same moment they raised their bows. Seeing this Liu Pei rode off at speed and as night was coming on, sought refuge with a friendly hermit nearby. But even before the tale of his escape was told, Tilu was patted and rubbed down and received a double ration of food as he nuzzled against his master's still dripping clothes. His splendid leap which saved the future emperor of Minor Han has been told in song and story to the present day.

*Ssuma-Hui in the Mulberry Tree (plate 30)*

It was not long thereafter that Liu Pei heard of Chuko Liang's wisdom and sought him out. That astute gentleman had no wish for public life in the turbulent times and was hard to meet with though in the end he became the devoted councillor of Liu Pei. In the course of the search, however, Liu met a number of philosophers and hermits who asked only that the world pass them by. An amusing side light are the few lines about Ssuma-hui who loved philosophy and cared little for physical comfort. Even hermits, however, must eat, so he went out one morning to a full fruited mulberry tree not far from his rustic hut. Climbing into the higher branches, he hung his basket on a limb and started picking. But then he heard the rustle of someone approaching and, peering down, saw his friend and crony Pa Tang. Greetings were exchanged, but all in a moment, they were launched into a full blown philosophical discussion. So while bees buzzed among the mulberries, warblers disputed on a limb close by and even a curious rabbit approached below, Pa Tang stood at the foot of the tree and Ssuma-hui leant in argument from his branch, once or twice nearly taking a header, they discussed deep philosophical arguments all day long, till evening shadows deepened and they discovered they were hungry. There were not even many mulberries for supper! It is but a glimpse but a charming one. Not all was blood and slaughter in these turbulent times.

Yet there were grim moments and sometimes a woman had to face them also. In the kingdom of Wu, the brother of the ruler, Sun I was prefect of Tanyang, beloved of his family but a cruel man when he had been drinking and harsh to his followers. When angered, he gave orders

Plate 29. *Liu Pei escapes assassination by making the impossible leap across the river Tan on his horse Tilu*

for floggings and so alienated his men that two of his officers who had a grievance against him plotted his assassination. There was to be an assembly of officials, but Sun I's beautiful wife was skilled in divination and begged him not to attend as the omens for the day were dangerous. However Sun I was obstinate and rode out with his followers. All went well and in returning he mounted his horse with sarcastic thought on the divination. But it was dusk and he did not see the faithless guardsman until the man was upon him and striking deep. Even as Sun I rolled from his horse, the real plotters rushed up and struck down the murderer. In Tanyang they entered Sun I's residence and were prepared to loot it. Coming upon Sun I's startled wife, the leading conspirator Kwei Lan was roused by her beauty, and changing his manner tried to make love to her, deploring the assassination and claiming he himself had avenged Sun I. But the young wife realized that her divination had indeed been too true. She stood for a moment white and trembling. Then her mind began plotting and she resorted to guile. Surely for proprieties sake she must make some show of mourning, later she might think of re-marriage. Thus attaining a respite, she dismissed Kwei Lan who fatuously thought he had found favor in her eyes. Wasting no time, she called in two faithful generals of her husband's and told her tale. She bowed before them weeping and they were much moved and promised their aid. The day of sacrifices for Sun I came and she performed them with ceremony, but afterwards she talked and laughed aloud and to Kwei Lan's smug satisfaction thinking of coming pleasure, asked him to supper. Retiring she put off her mourning and dressed herself in rich costume, assuming an allure toward her guest. Well she entertained him at supper and skilfully plied him with heavy wine. He became drunk and amorous, and took no notice of the fact that she more than once turned nervously toward the hanging curtains behind her. As Kwei Lan sought to put his arms around her, she cried out "Where are you, my generals?" and her two protectors rushed out with drawn swords. The drunken man was easily dispatched and the two officers wiped their bloody swords on the silk embroidered curtains. The wife of Sun I put on again her morning garb and with her own hands hung the head of Kwei Lan like a sacrifice before her husband's coffin. Yes, those times were grim indeed.

*Sun I's Wife*
*Entraps Kwei Lan*
*(plate 31)*

Plate 30. *The hermit Ssuma Hui, sitting in a mulberry tree philosophizing with his friend Pa Tang*

The course of war favored now one side, now another of the three kingdoms Wei, Wu, and Shu and there were often advisors who gave opinions for or against giving battle or retiring or even surrendering in the hope of safer gain later on. Wu to the south had been watching Ts'ao Ts'ao gathering a large force which seemed to threaten like the black cloud of a thunderstorm on the horizon and the civil and military officials were of two minds as to the best course to take. The military were for a determined stand, the civil authorities were for surrendering and making good an alliance with Ts'ao Ts'ao. However at that time the kingdom of Wu was in friendly contact with Liu Pei of Shu and sent a message begging that his great general Chuko Liang come to consult with them. That clever diplomat saw his chance and appeared, urbane and smiling, as if he did not know that the surrender of Wu to the power of Wei would soon mean the destruction of Shu. He listened, relaxed but politely attentive while the others wrangled in argument and Chou Yu, the minister of Wu expressed his fears of the power of Ts'ao Ts'ao and his unwillingness to bring a disastrous war down upon his people. Listening for some time, Chuko Liang finally put in his word. "You are quite right" he said to Chou Yu. "Ts'ao Ts'ao has proved himself almost invincible and although my master, Liu Pei has vigorously opposed him, he has been in this most unwise and it is greatly to his detriment. I deplore it. Of course surrender is hardly to the dignity of Wu, it would only be a vassal kingdom. Still it is the only reasonable course before Ts'ao's might. I advise it."

*The Ladies Chiao
Eavesdropping
(plate 32)*

"There," exclaimed Chou Yu. "Chuko Liang knows the times and agrees with me."

Chuko Liang leant forward. "It should then be settled that way—and yet there is another which would accomplish your purpose and really be simpler—so very easy and involve so little, a boat across the river to ferry over two people."

"What?" asked Chou Yu.

"Ah," answered Chuko Liang. "Surely you know that Ts'ao Ts'ao is a good judge of women and likes to be surrounded by beauties. Why else has he built the new Bronze Pavilion except for their pleasure and his own? What woman could resist its attraction—a marvellous place evident-

Plate 31. *The wife of Sun I and Kwei Lan, who had had her husband murdered, and who then killed the bravo who did the deed, pretending he had been loyal. She appeared to yield to his love-making but had hidden her generals nearby so that they could kill Kwei Lan when he became intoxicated.*

ly. And it is true that there are two women here, he met them once and quite set his heart upon them. I believe he coaxed his son who is a fair poet, you know, to write a poem upon them. The ladies would find themselves surrounded by luxury and adulation and you would have the gratitude and a lasting alliance with Ts'ao Ts'ao. What do you think? After all, what are two women compared with all the people in the country. The families could be compensated, and I suppose—" he broke off, smiling.

"And who are these two you suggest turning over?" demanded Chou Yu.

"Why, the Chiao sisters" answered Chuko Liang blandly.

Even then the same two ladies were listening, wide eyed and appalled behind the screen.

"The scoundrel!" exclaimed Chou Yu leaping to his feet.

Chuko Liang appeared bewildered. "Why surely—are two women so important?"

"You do not know" cried out Chou Yu. "One is the widow of the king and the younger my own wife!"

Chuko Liang looked astounded. "Indeed, how I have blundered! What a deadly fault, what a deadly fault!"

But as Chou Yu burst into fury at the insult Ts'ao had offered, Chuko Liang's veiled eyes had a brighter gleam in them.

There was no more talk at the council of allying Wu with Ts'ao Ts'ao.


But alliances were uneasy in those shifting days and Chou Yu still feared Ts'ao and mistrusted Shu and its too clever general. Attack on Ts'ao was discussed at length and they trembled at his immense force. Moreover they lacked arrows which they held to be the best weapon in river fighting. Chou Yu put their plight before Chuko Liang and asked if he could supply a hundred thousand arrows immediately.

"Who could make them in ten days! Yet ten days is too long a time. Ts'ao Ts'ao will have moved south by then" exclaimed Chuko Liang. "Have your men ready to receive them in three and the arrows shall be delivered."

"You are joking" said Chou Yu. "One does not wisely joke in war."

Plate 32. *Chuko Liang prevents an alliance between Wu and Wei by revealing Ts'ao Ts'ao's interest in the ladies Chiao, one the wife of Chou Yu and the other the wife of the king. Shown here are the ladies, listening from behind the screen.*

"Have five hundred small boats on the river three days hence to convey the arrows. They will be ready." And Chuko departed.

"The man is insane, he has sworn before the council. I consider that he has but signed his own death warrant. My men shall not help him to the arrows." Thus Chou Yu, for he had begun to fear Chuko as much as the enemy.

But Chuko sought out one of the lesser generals. "I think" he said "you have gotten me into this. How can I produce a hundred thousand arrows in three days? It is up to you to help me out."

The general stammered "I had not meant—How can I ever rescue you?" For he too was afraid of Chuko.

"I want" answered Chuko sternly, "a score of vessels manned by thirty men each. Their sides are to be lashed with straw and there are to be blue cotton screens behind it. See that you fail me not. On the third day I must have the arrows ready."

The general stood gaping, there seemed no possible connection between boats and the needed arrows, but he obeyed.

The night was densely foggy and the boats swift. They moved out down the Yangtze and their small crews feared, but the current carried them toward the great forces of Ts'ao Ts'ao. As they approached the camp, drums were beaten derisively and Ts'ao's forces startled but could only perceive dim shapes bearing down upon them. Fearing a ruse they waited and not venturing up the river, shot fast their arrows into the advancing boats. Presently the small boats were bristling with arrows like clumsy porcupines and Chuko Liang gave orders to turn their prows so that the further sides got the full effect of the shooting. The porcupines were complete. Even as the fog lifted a little, the sails were raised and the boats slipped away. As they did so, the crews shouted across the water derisively "We are grateful for your arrows, Sir Minister."

"We have more than we hoped for" said Chuko with satisfaction. "To-morrow Ts'ao shall have all his arrows back, to his great inconvenience."

"The man is a magician" sighed Chou Yu to the men of Wu.

In the latter part of the San Kuo when the alliances of war had come nearly full turn, Kuan Yu had been treacherously captured in an ambush

Plate 33. *Obtaining weapons by strategy*

by the men of Wu and executed because he would not yield his loyalty to his sworn brother, Liu Pei. He had even called the ruler of Wu a red bearded rat in proud defiance. So he went to his death, a beloved figure in Chinese history in whose grandeur and bravery the humble folk even today have found solace. He is the god of war who would prevent war and succor the oppressed.

Chang Fei went almost mad with grief at the loss of Kuan Yu and made such unreasonable demands upon his men with floggings and severest punishments that he was assassinated by two of his own men. And Liu Pei was left with his double grief to face a lonely world and realize that the great dynasty of the Han had become in the third century no more than a ghost. It would never be restored to its former glory. He died soon after at the age of sixty three and left his young son to the care and protection of Chuko Liang who now becomes the central figure of the novel. Were it not for the vivid accounts of the cunning and magic contrasted with the very human qualities of Chuko, the story would fall very flat after the death of the three heroes. But Chuko carries the tale.

One of his most picturesque exploits is the campaign into upper Burma against the wild tribes of the Mons. Shu was at that time peaceful and tranquil under the able administration of Chuko Liang, for the young king, son of Liu Pei, depended entirely upon the wise old minister. But when the Mons invaded Szechuan from the south and even won over the Prefect of Chien nung, Chuko realized it was more than a mere foray and felt he must lead a real punitive expedition.

"They are a barbarous and most uncivilized lot" he explained "and when to be harsh and when lenient must be left to the spur of the moment. I can not easily give instructions to some other man."

So they marched south, conciliating their own prefects by the rigidly correct behavior of the army and quieting the restless ones near the border. Soon they were in the steaming jungle and the fighting became an endurance of unaccustomed conditions as well as of subtle strategy.

*Chuko Liang in Burma (plate 34)*

The king of the Mons, Menghua, was a barbarian whose men fought naked, but he himself assumed considerable splendour. He wore a headdress inlaid with gold, a gold lion clasp at his belt and his pointed boots were green, his robes fine silk and his sword was chased with a pine tree

Plate 34. *Chuko Liang in Burma*

pattern. His horse was small, almost a pony, but fuzzy haired and of a vicious temper toward everyone except his master. The little beast was quick on the turn and clever on the difficult jungle paths. Sometimes however Menghua rode a water buffalo.

When Menghua first met the army of Chuko Liang, he looked down from a height and shrugged to his captains, "Why I had heard that Chuko was a great general, but his array is not so much. Look at those banners, all is confusion and their weapons are no better than ours. We should drive them back into their own country with ease."

And so it seemed for the army of Shu gave way before them and fled a score or so of li before the Mons came near enough to fight. Suddenly, however, Menghua's men found themselves surrounded and were given no chance to make a stand. Even Menghua was driven into a difficult ravine and captured, and a great number of prisoners taken. Trembling the Mons were brought before Chuko Liang who received them in imposing state, but ordered their bonds loosed, to their great amazement and offered them food and wine.

"This is the fault of your chief who has led you astray" said Chuko, "even now your mothers, your wives and children are weeping over your capture and expecting news of your deaths. They are weeping bitter tears for you. Yet I know you to be a simple people and well disposed if better led. So I mean to set you free. Go home and comfort your families, and here is a present of grain to take to them." So he dismissed them and they departed, some even weeping in their gratitude.

Then Menghua in chains was brought before him, hustled by the guards and defiant in his humiliation for even a barbarian chieftain can be proud.

"Will you submit?" demanded the Minister. "What would you do if I freed you?"

"Order my army again and return to the fight. Your Emperor did me a wrong in taking the territory where my people had lived for ages. Given the opportunity to fight again, why should I not attack?"

Chuko Liang watched the angry chief for a moment, then smiled and ordering him freed, gave him a caparisoned horse and sped him on his way, with a guide, to his own camp.

"Perhaps it will not be too difficult to capture you again" he said.

Plate 35. *Menghua's surrender to Chuko Liang*

Menghua's men were indeed glad to see him, but astonished and taken in by the ruse of his lie that he had escaped by his own cunning and stolen the horse he was riding. He sent for his brother and together they plotted to deceive Chuko Liang into thinking they had yielded and were sending tribute. He gathered together a considerable treasure of gold and pearls and rhinoceros horn and sent a hundred men with his brother. Chuko clapped his hands in seeming appreciation but he saw through the plot and was not deceived. He complimented them upon their offerings and entertained them with beef and flesh and wine. Two of the men returned to Menghua and reported how well, indeed sumptuously they had been received.

Menghua sure that his enemy would no longer be on his guard, marched at midnight with his men in three divisions to surround the Shu camp.

"We shall have them" he exclaimed in satisfaction, but the camp lay before them, deserted.

There was no opposition, not a soul was stirring. Yet the largest of the tents was brilliantly lit and, puzzled, they lifted the flap and pushed in. There lay Menghua's brother and all his men dead drunk. The wine had well drugged. The disgusted Mons picked them up like so many puppets and turned to go, but at that torches flared and drums began to clang.

In their panic many of the Mons threw down their arms and fled, only to find themselves surrounded on three sides by the army of Shu. Menghua managed with a few men to reach the river and saw a bark on the stream manned by Mons. Making a wild leap for it, he was dragged aboard, only to be bound and gagged. The boatmen were men of Shu in disguise.

Brought again before Chuko, the general grinned at him. "Your ruse was too shallow. Did you not think I should see through it? It is time you yielded." But again Menghua would not.

"Well, I shall still let you go this time" said Chuko with a shrug of the shoulders. "But remember, someday you will be in real danger."

It would be wearisome to tell the tale too fully, the plots and counter-plots, the dangers Chuko's own men fell into in the mysterious jungle, when poisoned waters overcame many of the soldiers where malaria rose in the evening mists and insects buzzed around them. There were strange encounters too with a chieftain who had trained the fiercest of wild beasts

Plate 36. *The azure banners of Liu Pei*

to fight for him. The men of Shu found themselves advancing against tigers, leopards and wolves who appeared like magic, clawing and snarling at the enemy, yet disciplined toward their masters who drove them. Terror spread among Chuko's forces but the general had his answer for he had heard of these. He had a score or more of red carts in which were hidden a few men but with them mechanical wild beasts whose mouths were stuffed with inflammables.

Next morning it was the men of Shu who attacked. Confident Menghua and the other chief met them with his terrible cohorts, but now it was Shu's turn and the real beasts saw furies in their own shapes, descending upon them breathing fire and black smoke so that the tigers and wolves and crouching leopards turned tail and fled back upon their masters causing great destruction.

The time came however when the great Chuko seemed to have exhausted all his skill, his men faced the Mons, then retreated, throwing away their arms. Afterwards they even abandoned a great number of black carts of supplies. When the Mons surrounded these eagerly, they suddenly burst into flames and soon the whole valley was filled with fire and the slaughter of the Mons was fearful.

Menghua fled and managed to escape apparently, but was soon waylaid in his wild gallop and there was a small chariot surrounded by only a few men. In it sat a white robed man holding no weapon but a feather fan. Again Menghua fled but was quickly captured and brought into camp where were other prisoners, his wife, his brothers and several of the chiefs. Crushed, he looked about him in despair, when a messenger appeared and addressed him. "The Minister is ashamed, there was too great slaughter in the ravine, which saddens him. He does not even wish to see you. Try yet again to take up the fight if you will. I am to release you. You are free to go."

*Manghua's Surrender*
*to Chuko Liang*
*(plate 35)*

But this time Menghua yielded. "Seven times have I been captured and seven times released. I am a barbarian and beyond the pale, but I have some sense of rectitude. How can I not surrender?"

And he threw himself down before Chuko's tent, exclaiming, "Oh, Minister, you have the majesty of Heaven. We men of the south will never again offer you battle—your mercy is even as the depth of the sky."

Plate 37. *Mu Lan, the young girl who took her father's place in the troops fighting on the northwest frontier in the 5th century A.D.*

Such indeed was their gratitude that they even erected a shrine to their conqueror and sacrificed to him at the four seasons.

Chuko Liang returned home and received more honors from the young king, Liu Pei's son. By fighting, subtle intrigue, sometimes apparently even by magic, he carried on his campaigns against Wei which waxed evermore powerful. But he died at fifty two. Even in death he outwitted Ssuma I, the crafty general of Wei, for Chuko had ordered a wooden image of himself put into his white horsed chariot which rode with the troops and created an appearance which could still strike awe into the enemy.

Ts'ao Ts'ao had not quite dared to set himself upon the vacant Han throne but left it to his son to take over. But with Chuko's death the heart had gone out of the matter and though Shu still had some able generals, they proved in the end no match for the engulfing power of Wei. Wu was in like case and for a time the Ts'ao clan was in ascendant but its own general Ssuma Yen turned on the king and forced his abdication, setting up the state of Chin which soon conquered Wu and re-united all China.

The Han was gone, the three states of Wei, Wu and Shu had vanished and a new cycle had begun.

*Azure Banners of Liu Pei·*
*(plate 36)*

But for those of us who love the old days and whose hearts were stirred by the hope of the restoration of the Han, the troops of Shu still ride the mountain passes where feathery bamboos bend over turbulent streams and above, dark leaved white roses shine against the cliffs. Kuan Yu still rides the Red Hare, his spear at ready, the war drums of Liu Pei echo from the heights and his azure banners still flaunt their victories as the winds sweep down from the hills of Szechuan.*

The dynasty of Chin was not destined to continue in full control of China for long. When the court of Loyang became a nest of intrigue, the northern barbarians entered the field and northern China fell under the

* It may be of interest to know that the description of the gorges in the mountains of Szechwan is not imaginary but exactly as given me by my father, Dr. Bailey Willis, the geologist who went down through Shensi and Szechwan in the spring of 1904 on an expedition of which he was head, for the Carnegie Institution of Washington.

Plate 38. *Chang Seng Yü painted dragons but did not put in the eyes.*

sway of petty kingdoms. Much of it between the Great Wall and the Yangtze river was ruled by the Toba tribe of Tartars. The dynasty was called Northern Wei and noted for its Buddhist sculpture in the caves of Yungkang and at Lungmen and much of this is left even today. These tribes had acquired a certain depth of Chinese civilization and with their ardent Buddhism had inspired great interest in it that sent the Chinese travelling to India in search of the true versions of Buddhist scriptures which they brought back as sacred objects. But in the difficult years when the unresting tribes made constant invasions of China's northern provinces, there were often calls for troops and officers to oppose the enemy on the northwest frontier.

At one time a certain provincial official was called upon to face their inroads but lay gravely sick at home, and it was a slight boyish figure whose warrior's dress seemed to fit ill upon him, who answered the summons in his stead. So youthful was his appearance, that one might have wondered whether his commands could secure obedience in his men. But *Mu Lan, Intrepid Fighter* they soon found a keenness and leadership that belied his youth and a *(plate 37)* boldness almost amounting to recklessness, that led to victories against odds. He became a beloved and honored leader and rose high in the ranks of Chinese troops who followed where he led.

Twelve years of fighting and manoeuvers against the tribes, of lonely vigils in the mountains, and forays when the barbarians least expected them, left him fit and hardened to endurance, yet still youthful in appearance under his warrior's helmet. Then came a lull in the campaigns and the young officer returned home to an eager family ready to applaud his prowess.

But for the feast that night, came from the women's quarters a fair young woman, poised and self-possessed, in rich silks with hair dressed high and jade ornaments that tinkled as she moved. It was the daughter of the house, Mu Lan.

"How good to wear women's dress again after twelve years" she said.

Painting in China is in legend first ascribed to a woman, rock painting with earthern colors, but that is in the far distant mists and more of it is not known. "Alas" says a later scholar "that so noble an achievement

Plate 39.   *Meng Hao Jan,   poet  and scholar of about*
*696 A.D., goes hunting for plum  blossoms in the snow.*

should have been initiated by a mere woman." So little of painting through the first thousand years of A.D. has survived, that one is left to judge most of them by early critics' descriptions or copies by enthusiasts who had no thought of plagiarism but rather a joy in the older tradition.

There are to be sure, certain tomb frescoes and delightful Han tiles which though their techniques may be limited, show a verve and spirit and joy in the essence of a scene, rarely found in later work and not even approached by the stiff and formal figures of early European painting.

Even the lightest discussion of Chinese art by a critic would go into the brilliant line technique of the Chinese painter, of his use of space, of his paints, ink and brushes, some of them mouse whiskers, of his marvels of shading with ground India ink, but it is not for the teller of tales to put himself to shame by entering that field.

Only, he would speak of the painter's effort to express the essence of his subject rather than its superficial form and except as the artist's own character must unconsciously flow into his work, his subject must become a living thing to confront the painter with a life and power of its own, capable in some cases of independent action.

This is well illustrated in an amusing anecdote of Chang Seng Yu, a sixth century artist. Most of his work was of Buddhist subjects and the one or two which have supposedly survived have a vividness and urgency about them worthy of a great painter.

But it is of the dragon frescoes on the wall of a palace, long since gone to dust, that the tale is told. The Emperor had ordered them and when they were finished viewed them with admiration, but on looking on them more closely was puzzled and then displeased.

*Chang Seng Yü and the Painted Dragon (plate 38)*

"But the dragons though fine and fiercely writhing beasts, have no eyes," he exclaimed.

"Your Majesty, those I cannot in wisdom put in, they would come alive."

The Emperor peevishly insisted, what was the good of beasts without eyes. Reluctantly and somewhat fearfully Chang Seng Yü obeyed the behest. His brush had scarcely completed its last stroke, the eyes glared down at them, when there was a rumble and a crack as of an earthquake. The dragon's claws writhed across the wall, its teeth ground savagely,

Plate 40. *Yang Ti's game of chess disrupted by Lady Wen Fei's dog*

and as the frescoe broke and fell in pieces before them, the dragon roared up through the roof of the palace and disappeared into the lowering skies above.

Another emphasis in Chinese painting was Man's oneness with Nature. He is not set apart as in the West as a superior being in a special spiritual category of his own, but is rather an integral and natural part of the world he lives in. While there are sometimes overwhelming forces inimical to him, there is a sympathy with mountains, cliffs and streams, gnarled pines and graceful bamboo as shown in the great landscape paintings of the Sung, Yuan, and Ming dynasties that bring the thrill of great creative expression to us today even as when they were first painted.

"Nature loves the wanderer who goes whistling on his way," writes one artist in a critique of painting.

*Meng Hao Jan in Search of Spring (plate 39)*

So Meng Hao Jan, the poet who lived at the end of the sixth century and loved the streams, mooring his tiny boat in the mist or wakes, light hearted, to hear all around the singing of birds, becomes a beloved figure as he goes forth on his donkey in search of spring, and he is often pictured thus. The snow is falling, it is already heavy on the ground and the mountains are but dim shapes in the whiteness. The old pines show a film of white. Still his patient donkey plods along and Meng Hao wraps himself more closely in his red cloak. And there it is before him, a single branch with tiny buds of the plum just showing pink petals among the falling flakes. Spring is on its way and Meng Hao turns homeward with a contented heart.

Until almost the end of the sixth century, China continued to be divided into a number of small kingdoms known as the Six Dynasties. The barbarians had come in in the north, but most of the group who were in control at this time had been much influenced by Chinese civilization and were moreover ardent Buddhists, so there was much activity in art inspired by Buddhism and much of the best of Chinese sculpture was created at this time and still has survived in northern Shansi and near the old capital of Loyang.

But in 581, the ambitious Yang Chien, Duke of Sui, consolidated north

Plate 41. *T'ai Tsung of the T'ang receives the tribute of the king of Uighurs. The little dogs were trained to bring in the white horse.*

China and a few years later brought all the country under one sway and founded the Sui Dynasty. Its power was destined to be brief for it lasted only until 618 and yet it was a brilliant epoch and ushered in one of the most glorious periods of Chinese history, the T'ang Dynasty.

Art flourished and at Tunhuang in the northwest where Buddhist frescoes had been painted through several centuries, the Sui paintings stand out in striking beauty.

The second Emperor of the Sui, Yang Ti had neither the frugality nor wisdom of his father, but spent huge sums and crushing labor for the people on imperial palaces and a system of canals which linked Loyang with the cities of the Yangtze valley and bitterly oppressive the people found him. He was interested in advancing education and patronized literature. Yet the tale I have been told of him is pure frivolity and must serve for a better. The luxury of his palaces was great and Yang Ti took great joy in it and all the sophisticated pleasures of court life. Chess was his favorite pastime and he and certain of the courtiers spent long hours over it. It was an autumn afternoon when the silken curtains were drawn against drafts and the scented braziers were welcome, that Yang Ti sat down with a worthy opponent across the ivory board. At first the pieces moved swiftly, play answered play and the Emperor smiled his satisfaction feeling sure of the game. The Lady Wen Fei sat nearby. She watched with interest, very intent, for she too was a skilful player. When the moves were long, she stroked the ears of her tiny sleeve-dog, O-Hsien curled up among her draperies and poking a cold nose into her hand for attention. The game went smoothly and the Emperor kept nodding his head, pleased with his own subtlety. But he had laid his flank bare and a bold move on the part of his opponent betrayed his queen—the next move meant disaster. In consternation, Yang Ti eyed the board, there seemed no move that could retrieve the game. A sudden motion beside him caused him to look up. Wen Fei rose, her long sleeves shimmering in the light of the candles, and O-Hsien landed sprawling in the midst of the board, the chessmen flying in all directions. The Emperor threw his head back in hearty laughter. "Ying!" (checkmate) he cried to his opponent. But the Lady Wen Fei shook her head at the little dog severly. "Why O-Hsien when did you you ever learn to play chess?" she exclaimed.

Plate 42. *The Princess Wen Chen in Tibet shocked by the Shamanistic rites at the court of Srong-Tsan*

But the frivolous must give way to a greater dynasty, when China stood head and shoulders in culture above the rest of the world.

Yang Ti's excesses in expenditure and overambitious schemes within the empire and in military undertakings had severly burdened the Chinese people and led to growing unrest. In an inspection of his northern provinces in 615, he was nearly captured by the Turks. He escaped but was forced to flee southward and revolts broke out across the country. He abdicated in 617 in favor of his grandson, a callow boy, but within a month the great Duke of T'ang had taken over the imperial power and the T'ang dynasty was established to continue for three hundred years one of the most brilliant and glamorous periods of world history.

The Duke of T'ang was a statesman and solider of unusual ability but he had four even more able sons, of whom the second, Li Shih-Min, had distinguished himself in leading the troops at only sixteen and thereafter became the guiding hand in the new dynasty. He succeeded in making a treaty with the Kagan of the Turks and came out victor in strife with his brothers so that his father abdicated in his favor in 626.

T'ai Tsung as he is known to history restored the prosperity of the Empire and placed China in the forefront of world powers. He was at once warrior and statesman, scholar and wise legislator, and above all knew how to handle men. He had trained officials and even the sons of barbarian and Korean rulers flocked to his Imperial University. Chang-an, his capital was thronged with foreign tradesmen from all of the Eastern World and they were given fair treatment and brought great wealth to the city and the Empire. Here he is receiving tribute from the Uighurs *Tribute of the Uighurs* who lived in the grasslands beyond the Gobi desert. The Uighurs had been *(plate 41)* called in China "Kaoche," High Carts, because they used large wheeled vehicles but their wealth lay in their fine horses and of these they sent tribute to the great Emperor. Tiny toy dogs were trained by their masters to lead the noble beasts by their bridles and T'ai Tsung, a lover of fine horses delighted in their skilful manoeuvering.

The Emperor had the wisdom to conciliate his neighbors as far as possible and to play off one barbarian tribe against another. He was also a generous victor and even gave the defeated Turkish princes Chinese titles and incorporated some of their troops into the Chinese army.

Plate 43. *Princess Wen Chen who married the King of Tibet and brought Buddhism to that country in 640 A.D., is deified.*

The Tibetans in their mountain fastnesses had achieved a certain unity at the end of the sixth century and by the middle of the seventh were in a position to harass the great South Route so important to the Chinese in their trade with western Asia. The Tibetan king, Srong-tsan Gampo sent an embassy with tribute to the Emperor but when he demanded a Chinese princess for wife, he was refused and invaded the western frontier. T'ai Tsung drove him back but in 640 yielded in the matter of an Imperial princess and sent him as bride the lovely Wen Chen, a relative of the Emperor himself. She must have had something of the intrepid character of the great Emperor. What a weary journey across the arid western provinces and the storm ridden mountain passes where snow and sleet poured down and the cold and damp penetrated even the furred robes of the princess. The horses slithered dangerously on muddy ledges and some of the baggage animals fell to their deaths from the high cliffs. The journey ended on the Tibetan plateau, often shadowed in cold and gloom and Srong-Tsan Gampo proved to be the rough and ready barbarian more apt for war than acceptable as a mate and of a high uncertain temper. Wen Chen found established there another wife, a Nepalese but had the wit and grace to make friends and even alliance with her. Both the women were devout Buddhists and the Tantric Shamanism of Srong-tsan and his court was a shock to them. The bloody sacrifices and the wild and curious demon dancers were ghastly to them. Wen Chen exclaimed in disgust "Is that called religion? There is no such thing as religion in this country!"

*Wen Chen Shocked by Shamanistic Rites (plate 42)*

Srong-Tsan was not above being influenced by his two wives, both young and attractive, and was persuaded by them to introduce Buddhism into Tibet, drawing on intercourse with India. The ladies had their hearts' desire but it is said that the king was himself not changed at heart, but carried on his bloodthirsty wars with his neighbors whenever provocation was given him and he usually found plenty. But Buddhism was in Tibet to stay and if it would hardly be recognized by its gentle founder and remnants of the ancient Shamanism still clung to it like lichens, it adapted itself to the needs of a vigorous and patient people living in a harsh climate. Both the princesses died young and Wen Chen was deified as the White Tara, an emanation of the goddess of mercy, happy in a lamaistic paradise, strange destiny for a little Chinese princess.

*Princess Wen Chen Deified (plate 43)*

Plate 44. *The Empress Wu Hou, ruthless, wise, and just*

In China the great T'ai Tsung had died and Kao Tsung came to the throne. But there was a more dominant personality at hand and for the next fifty years the destinies of the Empire were controlled by the Empress Wu Hou, sometime concubine, then Empress of Kao Tsung. At T'ai Tsung's death, she had been consigned to a Buddhist convent, there to spend the rest of what proved to be a very long life. She stayed exactly three weeks. When a festival drew the new Emperor to the Buddhist foundation, she arranged an apparently accidental meeting. She was young and beautiful and supremely clever with results that might have been foreseen. The impressionable Emperor succumbed to her charm and she swiftly became the dominating influence at the palace, relegating him to pleasures and dissipation. The guidance of the Empire became hers. She was utterly ruthless and unscrupulous. Those who stood in her way were murdered and the later formal historians of Confucian tenets have exe-created her, so that in many histories she is held up as an epitomy of evil. Yet she was a wise and just ruler of the Empire and under her regency

*Wu Hou*
*Ruthless, Wise and Just*
*(plate 44)*

over two puppet emperors from 684 till her death in 705, China prospered and expanded. She was a devout Buddhist and went often to prayer at the temple through the graceful courtyard where the golden chain tree flung its brilliant blossoms in season to the sunlight. It was not until she was over eighty, just a few months before her death, that she at last retired to the convent where she was supposed to have spent a pious life. How different had been the intervening years.

One of the greatest reigns of Chinese history came in with the accession of Ming Huang in 712 A.D. He was the grandson of Wu Hou and forty years of his reign showed China at a shining pinnacle of culture when there was harmony of learning and literature with the luxury of the court and peace along its frontiers.

Now lived the great poets, Meng Hao Jan who sought the plum blossoms, Li T'ai Po and Tu Fu, three men whose singing words thrill us today even in clumsy translations. They sang of awesome nature and its beauties, of the joys of friendship, the sorrows of fair women, of the ghosts of dead palaces and the sad devastation and chill of war. But also and in yet more lyric vein, they told of the delights of the Court, of festivals and picnics

Plate 45. *Yang Kwei Fei on a white horse*

and the stateliness of ceremonies, but most of all of the beauty of dances before the Emperor and of one who danced as she did all things in perfection. Ah, how can one tell the tale? How follow the shining threads of its weaving until they are torn and stained and disappear?

The Emperor was not young when, it is told, he first saw Yang Kwei Fei bathing under a floating cloud of cherry blossoms. It mattered not too much that she was the concubine of one of his many sons. The young man could take another, but the Lady Yang became henceforth the favorite of his father.

Then began lyric days when all the court did honor to her charm and poets and courtiers and humbler folk vied with each other to give her pleasure or invent new joys for the royal lovers. No effort was too great. The favorite wished fresh lichie nuts and relays of messengers, their mounts at gallop over the mountain passes, were sent into far Szechuan to bring them to her. She and her sisters loved riding and the finest horses carried the Emperor and Yang Kwei Fei with a gay company through winding ways of the palace park. There were exquisite dances of "rainbow skirts," a shimmer of gorgeous color under flowering trees, but none so lovely as when Yang Kwei Fei danced with white cockatoos under the willows in the gardens of the summer palace. The Emperor no longer gave early audience, but dallied with the Lady Yang behind silken curtains and some of the decisions of the Empire slipped into the hands of the powerful new minister, the favorite's brother.

*Yang Kwei Fei on a White Horse (plate 45)*

There was yet another whose coming was with giddy laughter and no one then foresaw what the end would be.

An Lu Shan was a Turk born beyond the Great Wall in the country of Liao Tung. He was captured as a boy and sold as a slave to a Chinese officer but his cunning and ability promoted him in the army and he finally rose to officer's rank. Though legends picture him as a romantic hero, splendid with red beard, huge of stature and superb in glittering armor, history tells rather of his gross fat and the outward guise of a buffoon which hid great cunning. To please the Emperor and the Lady Yang he was willing to play the clown and ingratiate himself until in delighted foolery she adopted him as a "son." Life was gay and licentious with practical jokes verging often on the indecent, but the Emperor looked on

*Yang Kwei Fei Dancing on the Terrace (plate 46)*

Plate 46. *Yang Kwei Fei, beloved of Ming Huang, dancing on the terrace of the Summer Palace*

complacently. The first minister, Yang Kwei Fei's brother, suspected him of seditious intrigue but his protestations of innocence and devotion won Ming Huang completely and An Lu Shan received yet more honors. Three years passed. Then he threw off all pretence and with the splendid troops at his command captured Tung Kuan Pass and marched upon the capital.

The Court had no such trained troops as the rebel General and abandoning the sprawling city, fled toward Szechuan. Even the provision of food and adequate clothing was forgotten in their haste, even the Emperor and his stricken lady lacked all comfort. The soldiers suffered, flight took endurance but did not call for the bravery of facing an enemy, they were hungry and dispirited. Mutiny broke out and the first victim was the all powerful Minister whom they murdered out of hand.

They threatened even the Emperor himself and cried out for the head of Yang Kwei Fei who had once admired An-Lu-Shan and been his friend. Terrified, worn with sleeplessness and fatigue, the Emperor weakly yielded.

It is said that the Lady Yang made humble obeisance before her lord and asked his permission to retire from his presence. Then with dignity and acceptance, she went forth alone to meet the soldiers and her fate. Jeering, they dragged her to a pagoda in the village and hung her to a slender pear tree which even her slight weight bent down. Her jewelled headdress and her girdle ornaments fell broken to the ground.

*The Tribute Horse*
*(plate 47)*

There is a very beautiful painting by an unknown artist called The Tribute Horse. A group of riders passes through a rocky landscape under high pines. The horses are beautifully caparisoned with rich saddle cloths that almost reach their hoofs and the riders speak to each other as if in need of companionship. In their midst is the finest horse of all, who steps proudly but daintily, picking his way among the rocks. The painting is called The Tribute Horse but may this not be a misnomer? Legend has it, that it represents the royal cavalcade as it flees to safety into Szechuan. The white horse has no rider. Yang Kwei Fei died on Ma Wei's slope.

The Emperor rides with bent head.

The teller of tales has touched not at all on Buddhism. It is too great a subject. It has its myriads of stories, its beauty of ritual, its devoted priests, its sutras for which the Chinese went as far as India and its five sacred

Plate 47. *The tribute horse*

mountains. Of one of these last, he would speak and tell the story of a miracle which has its charm.

In the middle of the ninth century, the Japanese monk, Ennin from the monastery of Mt. Hei in northern Japan went in an ambassador's train to China in the hope of bringing back "The Law" in sacred books and sutras to Japan. Their first attempts at reaching China were not successful, storms, pirates and hostile Chinese officials prevented them and it was only at last with the aid of friendly Korean Buddhists that they were able to reach Shantung. Fanatical Taoism was in ascendancy at the time under the half mad emperor Wu Tsung and Buddhism was persecuted as at no other time in Chinese history. Ennin and his accompanying monks went through many vicissitudes and trials before nine years later they were able to return to Japan, with a treasure of Buddhist texts and pictures, where Ennin himself was received with honor and was appointed Court Priest, and later became head of the mystic sect of Tendai Buddhism. From being but a wandering monk in search of the "Law" he became one of the greatest of Japanese clerics. While in China, in spite of official difficulties and obstacles which he and his fellow monks sometimes despaired of overcoming, Ennin was able to reach the great sacred mountain of the Wu Tai Shan in Shensi and stayed there some months.

He tells of the innumerable temples and monasteries spread over the five great peaks, of their ornate ritual with chanted music, of golden reliquaries and richly adorned altars. He rejoices in the coming of spring and the "brocade of flowers so fragrant that they perfumed men's garments as they passed." He had hoped to see miracles, that the gentle spirit of Manjusri, guardian Boddhisatva of the Mountain might manifest himself, a youth of beauty seated on a docile lion. The vision did not appear, but Ennin tells the story of a miracle long ago.

*Manjusri's Miraculous Appearance (plate 48)*

A great monastery, the Ta-hua-yen-ssu, was given what was called a "meagre feast" for the monks by a patron who hoped thus to gain spiritual acclaim for himself. On this occasion, however, beggars and laymen and the destitute crowded in for the feast. There were too many and the patron was angry and thought the ceremony mishandled. "I came to give offering to the monks" he said. "Why should I feed these others?" But the monks, more generous, persuaded him.

Plate 48. *Manjusri appearing miraculously on his lion before the monks*

A pregnant beggar woman sat down among them and on receiving her portion, demanded one for her unborn child. The patron cursed her for a fool and refused her. "Yet he is already a person" she answered. "I shall not eat if he may not" and she rose and made her way out of the hall while the monks looked on, perturbed. As she reached the door, a blinding light hid her and in her place appeared Manjusri, his "face of jade" like a great brightness. He was seated on a golden haired lion whose curls shone like the sun. A moment the vision quivered in the air above them, then as all the company flung themselves down in adoration, it thinned and slipped away into the skies above. Now everyone, laymen or nobles, beggars and humble folk were welcome at the monastery of Ta-hua-yen-ssu.

The rebellion of An-Lu-Shan had greatly weakened the T'ang dynasty. Ten years of war had devastated the countryside and the population was reduced to half. In 874 rebellion again broke out under an able and unscrupulous general who wasted the country and finally took Canton, capturing untold booty and massacring the inhabitants, even cutting down the mulberry trees that silk might not be made in the region. But decimated by fevers of the climate in Canton, his peasant troops melted away to their homesteads and the Emperor returned to Chang-an where the half ruined city had become the home of "hares and foxes." The rebel was assassinated in Shantung and it was his lieutenant who in 904 assassinated the Emperor and in 907 deposed the last of the T'ang princes. The south had long been divided and when the Kitans, a Mongol people gained part of the north, confusion reigned for some fifty years among small and shifting kingdoms.

In 960 a boy of seven was nominally Emperor and Chao Kuan Yin, a general, had been successful against the Kitans. He was loyal to the little puppet king. His own soldiers, however, forced his hand by surrounding his tent and electing him emperor. Dressing him in imperial robes, they took him in their midst to Kaifeng, the capital. Chao Kuan Yin assured the safety of the little former Emperor and his mother, before ascending the throne as the first Empeor of Sung and his whole reign showed the same skill and forbearance.

Sung had lost territory along its northwest border and was smaller

Plate 49. *Hui Tsung in the Palace Garden*

than in the T'ang Dynasty, but in culture it was again one of the great periods when art flourished in supreme beauty and the Court became a stronghold of intellectual and philosophical reforms.

When Hui Tsung came to the throne in 1100 he was only nineteen. He is called the most cultured emperor China ever had. He interested himself in religion trying to bring Confucianism, Taoism and Buddhism into one. But he is best known for his Academy where artists vied with each other in painting and discussion of art and the Empeor presided. His own collection of paintings was catalogued and showed over six thousand pictures. But Hui Tsung was also a painter himself of great charm and something more than skill. If not one of the true "immortals," he yet may stand as a lesser deity with his exquisite birds, meticulously painted, of which several have come down to us. There is also a joyous group of scholars at an alfresco meal. His paintings suggest a life of gracious charm and joy in beauty.

*Hui Tsung in the Palace Garden (plate 49)*

But Hui Tsung was not a good administrator. The Court was isolated from the mass of the people who suffered from onerous exactions and there was great restlessness among them. The Emperor's policies proved fatal when he tried to recover Peking and brought in Tartars to aid him. He lacked all realism in the world of politics and opened the way for the Mongols to make good their conquest of China. If only he could have remained the dreamer in his garden, ordering the intangibles of religion and painting. His unwisdom was patent but he is still one of the most sympathetic characters in Chinese history. It makes his end the more poignant. His Mongol allies turned against him and swept in from the north to the Yellow River to the terror of the capital. Kaifeng, unprepared, was beseiged. Hui Tsung lost his head in the crisis and capitulated. Kaifeng was taken in 1126. The dreamer of drams with his eldest son was carried off to the forests of Manchuria to spend the rest of their days, for Hui Tsung nine long years, among the Jurchens, barbaric hunters of the northern wilds, where the dark forest and cruel snows surrounded them and hemmed the campfires closely. How often their aching thoughts must have gone back to the flowering gardens and richly wrought palaces of Kaifeng.

*Hui Tsung in Exile (plate 50)*

Plate 50. *Hui Tsung in Exile*

Kaifeng had fallen and many of its inhabitants fled the city. Among them was one, Hsiao Chao, a sometime artist and small official. He sought refuge in the T'ai Heng mountains to the west but found there was no livelihood there to be had among their rocky peaks and perforce turned robber preying upon travellers. A bold and brawny fellow, he was fairly successful and his victims continued their way, still alive but shorn of any valuables they might be carrying. However there had been a dearth of victims for some days and on a sunny morning Hsiao Chao was rejoiced to see a tall figure come into sight above him in the rocky defile. The strategy of waylaying him was easy and soon the wayfarer stood before him and handed over a rather lean bundle wrapped in checked cloth. The stranger stood at ease and bent a half amused, half quizzical gaze upon him. Hsiao Chao had roughly grabbed the bundle and opened it to find no treasure, only a bit of food and paints and brushes which tumbled out among the rocks. Then as he looked up, an exclamation on his lips, the wayfarer smiled and they both burst out laughing and bowed half ceremoniously. Soon they were talking eagerly and the great painter Li Tang shared his meagre fare with Hsiao and drew him on to go southward with him to Hangchow where the court of the Southern Sungs still held sway. And there among the beautiful gardens of the city, Hsiao too became a painter at the Court and received many honors. There soft winds blow and there the Southern Sungs held to their intellectual and artistic dreams for more than a hundred years. But Li Tang and Hsiao Chao painted rugged cliffs that soar into the heavens and roaring streams that descend in cascades and foam among gnarled pines, and a few of their pictures are left for our wonder today.

The Southern Sung still lost in idealism kept a dreamlike existence for a hundred years, but portents were growing in the north.

The ruler of the world, Genghis Khan, was born in a black yurt in outer Mongolia and who would have cast his horoscope as Scourge of Europe as far as Hungary and the conqueror of all north China. The Mongols have been called the cruelest race that has ever lived and left in their wake utter destruction of cities and massacre of their enemies to the last

Plate 51. *Tsiao Chao encounters Li Tang.*

man. Along the northern roads of China piles of whitened bones were heaped high, mute testimony to their fury.

Genghis Khan died too soon, from an injury in a fall from his horse, to complete the conquest of China but the war continued under his sons and it was under his grandson, Kublai Khan that the Sungs fell before their conquerors. Their generals might have been equal to meeting the Mongols but were held back by weak ministers. Kublai's army beseiged Hangchow and it fell in 1276. The boy upon the throne was strangely spared but put into a Buddhist monastery where he died peacefully nearly fifty years later. His younger brother was sheltered by the loyalists on junks hiding in remote harbors near Canton, but the end came. In April 1279 the Mongols surrounded the Chinese flotilla. There was no escape. One of the loyal courtiers came to the young Emperor.

"There is no way out" he said. "The Empire is doomed and your life should end with it. Your brother basely surrendered. That disgrace must be wiped out." And seizing the boy in his arms, he plunged overboard into the waves.

Kublai showed himself an enlightened ruler. Chinese civilization had won its victory over him and his administration "healed the wounds of a century of warfare." The prosperity of the country which had sunk to its lowest level was restored. But one has told the tale much better, one Messer Marco Polo and to him I would leave the story, for I cannot equal it. All honor to him.

Kubilai was one of the great emperors of China and his grandson was also of noble breed. But after him the Mongol emperors sank into sloth and debauchery favoring a debased Tibetan lamaism. They had come too far from the rugged virtues of their northern steppes and the wild free life on horseback.

The Chinese, kept from high office and still patriots behind a facade of philosophy, were stirring again. An unexpected leader rose in the person of Chu-Yuan-Chang, one who seemed least likely among the millions to become of note. He was the son of a poor farm laborer and his whole family had died in an epidemic. As a means of living he became a Buddhist monk but only a few years later cast aside his robes to become a

Plate 52. *Cheng Kuei Fei, a gentle soul*

rebel leader on the lower Yangtze. He won the populace over by his leniency and in 1356 took Nanking and a little later gained possession of all South China. Then he marched against Peking. The cowardly Mongol emperor fled and Chu-Yuan-Chang was proclaimed Emperor by his victorious troops. So began the Ming, the Bright Dynasty, most truly Chinese after a hundred years of Mongol rule. It has been called an imitative dynasty with none of the creative surge of the T'ang and Sung. and indeed it tried to reflect them and to take up where they had left off, effacing, mentally at least, the Mongol interlopers. But yet how beautiful are the paintings they have left to us, the lovely delicacy of their birds and flowers, their scrolls of travellers along the rivers, unfolding bit by bit the beauties of the landscape, and Chiu Ying's dream of fair women in his exquisite scenes of court life and palace gardens. Someone has said that Chiu Ying is beloved by the Chinese because he painted life as any cultivated Chinese would like to think it.

Of course there are many more stories, a whole other dynasty under the Manchus before the modern world creeps in with its crass values denying the poetry and philosophy of ancient times.

*Cheng Kuei Fei*
*a Gentle Soul*
*(plate 52)*

One more picture comes to mind, the lovely Cheng Kuei Fei, wife of the Emperor Wan Li (1585 A.D.), a gentle soul whose influence for good was loved in a corrupt Court. She sits in the luxurious beauty of a palace room, holding a wine cup in a frail hand, her tiny dog at her feet and an open doorway looking out upon the spring. She died young but her spirit held all the charm and suave beauty of the Ming.

And not so many years after Cheng Hua, the Bright Dynasty went down to miserable defeat before the Manchus as much because of its own dissensions as because of the power of the conquerors.

Shall we go into that tragedy and on beyond? Invention fails. The teller of tales is old and his voice falters. The shadows grow dark across the village square under the Wuting trees. Dim flickering lights appear in the nearby houses. The sunset has faded. There is no place now for the dreamer. He has talked too long.

Only someday, perhaps, the years will make full turn, and the Chinese

Plate 53. *Chinese junk sailing into the sunrise*

*Chinese Junk*
*Sailing into the Sunrise*
*(plate 53)*

junks sail once more into the sunrise on peaceful missions and the world be gay again remembering the glorious heritage of the past.

I can do no better than leave with you words from a bronze of ancient Chou: "Peace be with you wherever you go and of the open road may there be no end."

Farewell.